BOOKWORMS

Diamond

STORIES FOR READING CIRCLES
Stage 5 (1800 headwords) — Upp Int
Stage 6 (2500 headwords) — Adv.

The seven short stories in this book come from different volumes in the Oxford Bookworms Library. There are four stories at Stage 5 and three stories at Stage 6. All have been specially chosen for Reading Circles.

Here are stories from New Zealand, Ireland, America, and England. Here are people from all walks of life, with experiences to make us smile, or make us sad, or send a shiver up our spines. A child joins the war between her parents, taking her mother's side. A young woman goes to her first dance, her heart beating with excitement. Two respectable gentlemen conduct an experiment in thought transfer, with horrifying results. One man plots a murderous revenge, another man plans death by fire. But there is also the kindness of the heart, which can be found in unexpected places: the offer of food and shelter on a stormy night in Ireland; or a kind word and a resting place for a hunted man ...

OXFORD BOOKWORMS LIBRARY
Series Editor: Jennifer Bassett
Founder Editor: Tricia Hedge

To
The very first
Bookworms Club Reading Circle in Japan
Tina Ferrato (teacher / facilitator)
Satoshi Hikone
Kana Okubo
Mikiko Takamura
Miki Tanaka
Tang Wei (Elvis)
Kanae Yumita
who read and discussed the stories
in Bookworms Club Silver and who,
many years later, still meet in their reading circle
to talk about the stories they have read.

BOOKWORMS CLUB

Diamond

STORIES FOR READING CIRCLES

Editor:
Mark Furr

OXFORD UNIVERSITY PRESS

OXFORD
UNIVERSITY PRESS

Great Clarendon Street, Oxford OX2 6DP

Oxford University Press is a department of the University of Oxford.
It furthers the University's objective of excellence in research, scholarship,
and education by publishing worldwide in

Oxford New York

Auckland Cape Town Dar es Salaam Hong Kong Karachi
Kuala Lumpur Madrid Melbourne Mexico City Nairobi
New Delhi Shanghai Taipei Toronto

With offices in

Argentina Austria Brazil Chile Czech Republic France Greece
Guatemala Hungary Italy Japan Poland Portugal Singapore
South Korea Switzerland Thailand Turkey Ukraine Vietnam

OXFORD and OXFORD ENGLISH are registered trade marks of
Oxford University Press in the UK and in certain other countries

First published in Bookworms Club 2009
2013 2012 2011 2010
10 9 8 7 6 5 4 3 2

ISBN: 978 0 19 472008 3

Printed in China

ACKNOWLEDGEMENTS

*The publishers are grateful to the following for permission to abridge and simplify copyright
texts*: Knox Burger Associates Ltd for *Death Wish* by Lawrence Block first published
in *Alfred Hitchcock's Mystery Magazine*; Watson, Little Limited. Agency for *Cooking the
Books* by Christopher Fowler first published in *More City Jitters*; Brian Friel for *Mr
Sing My Heart's Delight* first published in *The Saucer of Larks*; Claire Keegan for *Men
and Women* first published in *Antarctica*; A. P. Watt Limited on behalf of the Literary
Executors of the Estate of H. G. Wells for *The Stolen Body* by H. G. Wells, from *The
Complete Stories of H. G. Wells*.

CONTENTS

SOURCE OF STORIES

The seven stories in this book were originally published in different volumes in the OXFORD BOOKWORMS LIBRARY. They appeared in the following titles:

Millie
 Katherine Mansfield, from *The Garden Party and Other Stories*
 Retold by Rosalie Kerr

Her First Ball
 Katherine Mansfield, from *The Garden Party and Other Stories*
 Retold by Rosalie Kerr

Men and Women
 Claire Keegan, from *Treading on Dreams: Stories from Ireland*
 Retold by Clare West

Mr Sing My Heart's Delight
 Brian Friel, from *Treading on Dreams: Stories from Ireland*
 Retold by Clare West

Death Wish
 Lawrence Block, from *American Crime Stories*
 Retold by John Escott

Cooking the Books
 Christopher Fowler, from *The Fly and Other Horror Stories*
 Retold by John Escott

The Stolen Body
 H. G. Wells, from *The Fly and Other Horror Stories*
 Retold by John Escott

~

Welcome
to Reading Circles

Reading Circles are small groups of students who meet in the classroom to talk about stories. Each student has a special role, and usually there are six roles in the Circle:

 Discussion Leader   Word Master

 Summarizer   Passage Person

 Connector   Culture Collector

Each role has a role sheet with notes and questions which will help you prepare for your Reading Circle discussions in the classroom. You can read more about the roles and the role sheets on pages 107 to 113 at the back of this book.

The stories in this book have been specially chosen for Reading Circles. They have many different themes, and students everywhere enjoy reading them and talking about them in their Circle. Everybody's ideas are important; there are no 'right' or 'wrong' answers when you are talking about stories.

Enjoy the reading, enjoy the talking – and discover the magic of Reading Circles …

Mark Furr
Hawaii, September 2008

Millie

~

If you lived on a lonely farm in New Zealand in the early 1900s, you had to be tough. The hot, dusty land was hard; horses, dogs, people were hard. If a murder took place, you might take the law into your own hands.

Millie Evans is a hard woman. You can see years of hot, hard farm work in her face, her hands. She can use a gun, she doesn't scare easily, not even at news of a murder ...

like a man

before/ during / after

meetig

KATHERINE MANSFIELD

Millie

Retold by Rosalie Kerr

Millie stood and watched until the men disappeared
from view. When they were far down the road,
Willie Cox turned round on his horse and waved to her.
But she didn't wave back. Not a bad young fellow, Willie
Cox, but a bit too free and easy in his ways. Oh, my word!
It was hot. Hot enough to fry your hair.

Millie put her hand up to keep the sun out of her
eyes, and looked out over the dry, burnt paddocks. In the
distance along the dusty road she could see the horses,
like brown flies jumping up and down. It was half-past
two in the afternoon. The sun hung in the pale blue sky
like a burning mirror, and away beyond the paddocks the
blue mountains trembled and jumped like the sea.

Sid wouldn't be back until half-past ten. He had ridden
over to the town with four of the farm boys, to help
find the young fellow who'd murdered Mr Williamson.
Such a terrible thing! And Mrs Williamson left alone
with all those kids. Strange! She couldn't believe that
Mr Williamson was dead. He was such a joker. Always
making people laugh.

Willie Cox said they'd found him in one of the farm
buildings, shot bang through the head. The young
English fellow who was with the Williamsons to learn

4

about farming had disappeared. Strange! Why would anyone shoot Mr Williamson? He was so popular. My word! What would they do to that young man when they caught him? Well, you couldn't feel sorry for him. As Sid said, if they didn't hang him, he could just go out and kill someone else. There was blood all over the place. Willie Cox said he got such a shock when he saw it, that he picked a cigarette up out of the blood and smoked it. My word! He must have been half crazy.

Millie went back into the kitchen. Slowly, she washed the dinner plates. Then she went into the bedroom, stared at herself in the piece of mirror, and dried her hot, wet face with a towel. What was the matter with her *changeable* that afternoon? She wanted to cry – about nothing! She decided to change her clothes and have a good cup of tea. Yes, that would help.

She sat on the side of the bed and stared at the coloured picture on the wall, *Garden Party at Windsor Castle*. In the middle of green lawns and shady trees sat Queen Victoria, with ladies in flowery dresses all around her. Behind them you could see the castle, with British flags flying from its towers. 'I wonder if it really looked like that.' Millie stared at the flowery ladies, who smiled coolly back at her. 'I wouldn't want their lives. Running round all day after the old Queen … '

On the table that Sid had made for her from packing cases, there was a photograph of her and Sid on their wedding day. Now that was a nice picture! She was sitting in a chair in her white dress, with Sid standing with one hand on her shoulder, looking at her flowers. Behind them there was a waterfall, and Mount Cook in the distance, covered with snow. She had almost forgotten her wedding day. Time passed so quickly, and with nobody to talk to …

'I wonder why we never had kids … Well, *I've* never missed them. Perhaps Sid has, though. He's softer than me.'

Then she sat quiet, thinking of nothing at all, with her red hands on her knees. *Tick-tick* went the clock in the silent kitchen. Quite suddenly, Millie felt frightened. A strange trembling started inside her – in her stomach – and then spread all over to her knees and hands. 'There's somebody outside.'

She went softly into the kitchen. Nobody there. The back door was closed. She stopped and listened, and the furniture seemed to stretch and breathe … and listen, too. There it was again – something moving, outside. 'Go and see what it is, Millie Evans.'

She ran to the back door, opened it, and just saw somebody run and hide behind the wood pile. 'Who's there?' she called in a loud, brave voice. 'Come out! I seen you! I know who you are. I've got my gun.' She was not frightened any more. She was terribly angry. Her heart banged like a drum. 'I'll teach you to frighten a woman,' she shouted, and she took a gun and ran out of the house, over to the wood pile.

A young man lay there, on his stomach, with one arm across his face.

'Get up!' She kicked him in the shoulders. He didn't move. 'Oh, my God, I believe he's dead.' She knelt down and rolled him onto his back. She sat in the dust, staring at him; her lips trembled with horror.

He was not much more than a boy, with fair hair and a light beard on his chin. His eyes were closed, his face covered in dirt and dust. He wore a cotton shirt and trousers; there was blood on one of his trouser-legs.

'I *can't*,' said Millie, and then, 'You've got to.' She bent over and felt his heart. 'Wait a minute,' she whispered, 'wait a minute,' and she ran into the house for brandy and a bucket of water. 'What are you going to do, Millie Evans? Oh, I don't know. I never saw anyone unconscious before.' She knelt down, put her arm under the boy's head, and poured brandy between his lips. It ran out at the sides of his mouth. She took a cloth and washed his face and neck with the cool water. Under the dirt and dust, his face was as white as the cloth, thin, and marked by little lines.

A strange and terrible feeling took hold of Millie Evans. Deep inside her chest, it grew like a plant after rain, and burst painfully into leaf. 'Feeling better? All right, are you?' The boy breathed sharply, his eyes opened, and he moved his head from side to side. Millie touched his hair. 'Feeling fine now, aren't you?' The pain in her chest made her breathless. 'It's no good crying, Millie Evans. You've got to be sensible.' Suddenly he sat up and pulled away from her, staring at the ground. 'There, there,' cried Millie, in a strange, shaky voice.

The boy turned and looked at her, still not speaking. His eyes were so full of pain and terror that she had to shut her teeth together hard to stop herself crying. After a long pause he said, in the voice of a little child talking in his sleep, 'I'm hungry.' His lips trembled.

She stood up. 'Come on into the house and have a proper meal,' she said. 'Can you walk?'

'Yes,' he whispered, and followed her slowly to the door. Then he stopped. 'I'm not coming in,' he said. He sat down in the shade of the house.

Millie watched him. 'When did you last eat?' He shook his head. She went and put meat and bread and butter on a plate, but when she brought it to him, he was standing up, looking around. He did not take the plate of food she held out to him. 'When are they coming back?' he whispered.

At that moment she knew who he was. She stood there, holding the plate, staring. He was Harrison, the English fellow who'd killed Mr Williamson. 'I know who you are,' she said, very slowly. 'I must have been blind not to see it from the start.'

He made a movement with his hands, which seemed to say, 'That's all nothing.' Again, he asked, 'When are they coming back?'

And she meant to say, 'Any minute now. They're on their way now.' Instead, she said to the poor frightened face, 'Not until half-past ten.'

He sat down and closed his eyes. Tears ran down his face. Just a kid. And all those men after him. 'Try a bit of meat,' Millie said. 'It's what you need. Get some good food in your stomach.' She sat down beside him, with the plate of food on her knees. 'Here – try a bit.' She broke the bread and butter into little pieces, and she thought, 'They won't catch him. Not if I can stop them. Men are all rotten. I don't care what he's done or not done. Do what you can to help him, Millie Evans. He's only a sick kid.'

wants to help

⚭

Millie lay on her back in bed, with her eyes open, listening. Sid turned over, pulled the sheet round him and said, 'Good night, old girl.' She heard Willie Cox and the other fellows drop their clothes on the kitchen floor, and then their voices, and Willie Cox saying, 'Lie down, lie down, you little devil,' to his dog.

l 8

The house grew quiet. She lay there and listened. It was hot. She was frightened to move, because of Sid. 'He must escape, he must. I don't care about the law and all that rubbish they've been talking about,' she thought angrily. She listened to the silence. He ought to be moving …

concerned for him

Before there was any sound from outside, Willie Cox's dog got up and went to the back door. A feeling of terror rose in Millie. 'What's that dog doing? What a fool that young fellow is with a dog here. Why doesn't he lie down and sleep?' The dog stopped, but she knew it was listening.

Suddenly, with a sound that made her cry out in horror, the dog started barking and rushing about. 'What's that? What's happening?' Sid got out of bed.

'It's nothing, it's only Willie's dog. Sid, Sid!' She took his arm, but he pushed her away.

'By God, there's something out there!' Sid quickly

pulled his trousers on. Willie Cox opened the back door, and the dog rushed madly out of the house.

'Sid, there's someone in the paddock,' one of the men shouted.

'What is it – what's that?' said Sid. 'Here Millie, take the lantern. Willie! There's someone in with the horses!'

escape The men ran out of the house, and at the same moment, Millie saw Harrison rush across the paddock on Sid's horse and down the road.

'Millie, bring that lantern, quick!' She ran out in her nightdress to give it to him. They were away down the road in a second.

And as she watched Harrison in the distance, and the men rushing after him, a strange and crazy delight came to her, drowning all other feelings. She ran into the road – she laughed and screamed and danced in the dust, waving the lantern in the air.

'After him, after him, Sid! Catch him, Willie! Go on, go on! Shoot him down! Shoot him!'

WORD FOCUS

These word jumbles have the letters in the wrong order. Put the letters in the correct order to make a word which will fit the gap in each sentence. Here is an example:

rkoje Mr Williamson was a *joker*, always making people laugh.

1 cpddoka Willie's dog heard someone in the _____, the field where the horses were kept.
2 lfwole The young English _____ was staying at the Williamsons' to learn about farming.
3 nlaws In the picture, Queen Victoria and her ladies were in the middle of green _____ and shady trees.
4 gibrkna Willie Cox's dog was making a lot of noise, _____ and rushing about.
5 ntrlaen When Sid rushed out into the dark to chase Harrison, he called to Millie to bring the _____ to him.
6 ikd Millie and Sid never had _____s, so Millie had never been a mother.
7 ghna Sid said they should _____ the murderer if they caught him.

The next day perhaps Millie wrote in her diary. Use five of the seven words above to fill the gaps.

I was shocked by the news that the young English ___ had killed Mr Williamson. But when I found him, he looked more like a ___ than a murderer. I can't explain why, but I had to help him. I felt so anxious when the dog started ___ last night, because I knew the boy was hiding in the ___. And then, when Sid asked me for the ___, my feelings began to change ... now, I just don't understand how I feel ...

STORY FOCUS 1

Authors will often allow characters to change their minds about the events or other characters in a story. In this story, Millie's attitude towards the murder and the murderer keeps changing. Think about these questions, and fill in the boxes below.

1 Can you find and write down three short passages which show how Millie feels about the murderer at different points in the story?

2 How do you think Millie feels at each of these points?

3 Can you suggest any causes for Millie's confused feelings?

1
2
3

STORY FOCUS 2

Imagine you are a reporter, and you have heard that Millie might know more about Harrison than she is telling. You can ask Millie five questions to find out what she knows. Which five questions will you ask her?

1

2

3

4

5

Her First Ball

~

Children who have no brothers or sisters sometimes lead lonely lives, especially if they live deep in the country, with no near neighbours. And for a shy young girl, the first steps out into the big wide world can be both exciting and alarming.

Leila is eighteen, about to go and stay with her cousins in town, where she will go to a ball that night – her very first dance. 'Oh, mother, I'm *so* excited … but … but I won't know *anyone* there! Do I *really* want to go? Oh, oh – where are my *shoes?*'

KATHERINE MANSFIELD

Her First Ball

Retold by Rosalie Kerr

Leila found it hard to say exactly when the ball began.
Perhaps it began in the car taking her there. It did
not matter that she shared the car with the Sheridan
sisters and their brother. She sat back in her own little
corner of it, and away she went, past dancing houses and
fences and trees.

'Have you really never been to a ball before, Leila? But
how strange—' cried the Sheridan girls.

'We lived so far from anyone else,' Leila said softly. 'In
the country we had no near neighbours.'

Oh dear, how hard it was to be calm like the others!
She tried not to smile too much; she tried not to care. But
everything was so new and exciting. Meg's roses, Jose's
necklace, Laura's little dark head above her white dress –
she would remember these things for ever.

Her cousin Laurie reached over and touched Laura on
the knee.

'Listen,' he said. 'We'll do the third and ninth dances
together, as usual. OK, darling?'

Oh, how wonderful to have a brother! Leila was so
excited that she suddenly wanted to cry, because she was
an only child, and no brother had ever said 'OK, darling?'
to her; no sister would ever say, as Meg said to Jose at

14

that moment, 'I've never seen your hair look so lovely as it does tonight!'

But there was no time to cry. They were at the hall already. The street was bright with moving lights and happy faces; little white shoes chased each other like birds.

'Hold on to me, Leila; you'll get lost,' said Laura.

'Come on, girls, let's go straight in,' said Laurie.

Leila put her hand on Laura's arm, and somehow the crowd carried them along and pushed them past the big golden lamp, along the passage and into the little room marked 'Ladies'. Here it was even more crowded and noisy. Everyone was pushing forwards, trying to get to the mirror.

There was a big gas light in the ladies' room. It wouldn't wait; it was dancing already. When the door opened, it jumped up almost as high as the ceiling.

Dark girls, fair girls were combing their hair, opening and closing bags, fastening buttons. And because they were all laughing, it seemed to Leila that they were all lovely.

'Aren't there any hairpins?' cried a voice. 'I need some hairpins.'

'Be a darling and put some powder on my back,' cried someone else.

'But I *must* have a needle and cotton! I've torn miles off my skirt!' screamed a third.

Then a voice said, 'Pass them along, pass them along!' and the basket of dance programmes went from hand to hand. Lovely little pink and silver programmes with tiny pink pencils. Leila's fingers shook as she took one. She

15

wanted to ask, 'Should I take one, too?' But then Meg cried, 'Ready, Leila?' and they pushed through the crowd towards the doors of the dance-hall.

The band was silent, waiting to begin playing, but the room was full of the noise of talking and laughter. Leila felt that even the little coloured flags which hung from the ceiling were talking. She forgot to be shy. She forgot how, earlier that day, she had sat on her bed with one shoe off and one shoe on and begged her mother to ring up her cousins and say that she couldn't come. The feeling she had had, that she wanted to go home, to be back at her dark lonely house out in the country, suddenly changed to a feeling of complete happiness that she was here at this ball.

She looked at the shining, golden floor, the flowers, the coloured lights, and at the stage, with its red carpet and golden chairs, and the band ready to play, and she thought, 'How lovely! How simply lovely!'

All the girls stood together on one side of the doors, and the men stood on the other side. Older ladies, in dark dresses, walked with little careful steps over the shiny floor towards the stage.

'This is my little country cousin Leila. Be nice to her. Find her partners. I'm looking after her,' Meg was telling all the girls.

Strange faces smiled sweetly at Leila. Strange voices answered, 'Of course, my dear.' But Leila knew that the girls didn't really see her. They were looking at the men. Why didn't the men begin? What were they waiting for?

They stood there, not talking, just smiling to themselves. Then quite suddenly, they were coming towards the girls, flying towards them over the golden floor.

A tall, fair man flew up to Meg, took her programme and wrote something in it. Meg passed him on to Leila. 'May I have the pleasure?' He wrote in her programme, smiled at her and moved on. Then a dark man came up to Leila, then cousin Laurie and a friend. Then quite an old man – fat and rather bald, too – took her programme and said, 'Let me see, let me see!' He looked at his programme, which was black with names, and at Leila's programme. He seemed to have so much trouble finding a free dance for her that Leila felt ashamed.

'Oh, please don't bother!' she said eagerly.

But the fat man wrote something in her programme and looked at her again.

'Do I remember this bright little face?' he said softly. 'Have I seen this little face before?'

At that moment the band began playing; the fat man disappeared. He was carried away on a wave of music that flew over the shining floor, breaking the groups of people into couples and throwing them out to the corners of the room.

Leila had learnt to dance at school. Every Saturday afternoon, the girls were taken to a little hall where Miss Eccles (of London) gave her 'top quality' lessons. But the difference between that poor little hall – with an old woman banging on the piano and Miss Eccles shouting at the girls to lift their feet – the difference between that

17

place and this wonderful place of music and golden light was so great that Leila felt she would die if she didn't dance soon.

'Our dance, I think.' Someone smiled and gave her his hand. She didn't need to die, after all. She floated away like a flower on a stream.

'Quite a good floor, isn't it?' said a voice close to her ear.

'I think it's most beautifully slippery,' said Leila.

'Excuse me?' The voice sounded surprised. Leila said it again. There was a tiny pause before the voice said, 'Oh, quite,' and they danced on.

He danced so beautifully. That was the great difference between dancing with men and dancing with girls, Leila decided. Girls bumped into you and stepped on your feet.

The flowers were no longer flowers; they were pink and white flags flying by.

'Were you at the Bells' last week?' the voice said. It was a tired voice. Leila wondered whether she should ask him if he needed to stop and rest.

'No, this is my first ball,' she said.

He gave a little laugh. 'Oh, I say!'

'Yes, it really is the first ball that I've ever been to.' Leila felt quite excited, just talking about it. 'You see, I've lived in the country all my life ... '

At that moment the music stopped, and they went to sit down. Leila's partner did not say very much. He stretched out his legs, played with a button on his jacket and looked around the room. But it didn't matter. The

band began to play again, and her second partner seemed
to appear from nowhere.

'Floor's not bad,' said the new voice. 'Were you at the
Neaves' last Tuesday?'

Again, Leila explained that this was her first ball. It
was strange that her partners did not seem to find this
more interesting. It was so exciting! Her first ball! She
was at the beginning of everything.

'How about an ice-cream?' said her partner. And they
went through the doors, down the passage to the supper-
room. Leila's face felt hot, and she was terribly thirsty.
How sweet the ice-creams looked on their little glass
plates, and how deliciously cold the spoons were!

When they came back to the hall, the fat man was
waiting for her by the door. It gave Leila quite a shock to
see how old he was; he ought to be on the stage with the
mothers and fathers. And when she compared him with
her other partners, his clothes looked old, too, and not
terribly clean.

'Come along, little lady,' said the fat man. He held her
loosely, and they moved so slowly that it was more like
walking than dancing. But he said nothing at all about
the floor. 'Your first ball, isn't it?' he said.

'How *did* you know?'

'Ah,' said the fat man, 'that's what it is to be old! You
see, I've been doing this for the last thirty years.'

'Thirty years!' cried Leila. Twelve years before she was
born!

'Terrible to think about, isn't it?' the fat man said

19

sadly. Leila looked at his bald head, and she felt quite sorry for him.

'I think it's wonderful that you can still dance so well,' she said kindly.

'Kind little lady,' the fat man said. He held her a little closer. 'Of course,' he said, 'you won't be able to go on as long as this. Oh, no,' said the fat man, 'long before you're as old as I am, you'll be sitting up there on the stage in your nice black dress, watching. And these pretty arms will be little short fat ones.' The fat man shook his head sadly at the thought. 'And you'll smile just like those poor old dears up there, and point to your daughter, and tell the old lady next to you how some terrible man tried to kiss her at a ball. And your poor heart will ache, ache' – he held her even closer, to show how sorry he felt for that poor heart – 'because no one wants to kiss you now. And you'll say how awful these slippery floors are, how dangerous to walk on. Yes, little lady?' the fat man said softly.

Leila gave a light little laugh, but she did not feel like laughing. Was it – could it all be true? Was this first ball only the beginning of her last ball? The music seemed to change. It sounded sad, sad. Oh, how quickly things changed! Why didn't happiness last for ever? For ever wouldn't be a bit too long!

'I want to stop,' she said in a breathless voice. The fat man led her to the door.

'No,' she said, 'I don't want to go outside.'

She stood there by the wall, trying to smile. But deep

inside her a little girl threw herself down on her bed and
burst into tears. Why did he have to ruin it all?

'I say, you know,' said the fat man, 'you mustn't take
me seriously, little lady.'

'Of course I don't!' said Leila, biting her lip. *trying not to cry.*

More people stood up to dance. The band was getting
ready to play again. But Leila didn't want to dance any
more. She wanted to be at home, looking out of her
bedroom window at the stars.

But then the lovely music started, and a young man
came to dance with her. She decided to dance with him
and then go, as soon as she could find Meg. Very stiffly,
she walked out onto the dance-floor. But in a moment her
feet simply danced away with her. The lights, the flowers,
the dresses, the pink faces, all became one beautiful
flying wheel. When her next partner bumped her into the
fat man, she just smiled at him happily. She didn't even
recognize him again. *Life goes on.*

not what I expected.

21

WORD FOCUS

Use the clues below and complete this crossword with words from the story.

ACROSS

3 Each girl at the ball was given a little pink and silver _____. The men wrote in it to schedule their dances.

5 The sweet frozen food that Leila ate at the ball was _____.

7 The musicians were on a ____, which is a raised platform.

DOWN

1 A _____ is a party for dancing with an organized programme.

2 Leila wished that she had a brother who would call her '_____'.

3 Leila's cousin Meg asked her friends to help find dance _____ for Leila.

4 In the story, Leila is _____ years old.

6 Before the dance, all the girls wanted to look at themselves one last time, so they were pushing forwards, trying to get to the _____.

STORY FOCUS

After the ball, perhaps Leila wrote in her diary. To read her diary entry, match these halves of sentences to make a paragraph of eleven sentences.

1 While I was listening to my cousins in the car, I wanted to cry ...

2 Then, suddenly, we arrived at the hall, jumped out of the car, ...

3 In the ladies' room, I received my programme, ...

4 But, as soon as we went into the dance hall, ...

5 Then, when the men started to hurry across the room, ...

6 But after only a few minutes, ...

7 I really enjoyed the first two dances, ...

8 My third dance, however, was different ...

9 He was a fat man ...

10 While we were dancing, ...

11 But now, I can't remember exactly what he said ...

12 and I was very anxious when I looked at it.

13 my dance programme was full.

14 because my next dance and the lovely music made me happy again.

15 who said he had been attending balls for thirty years.

16 and I even had ice-cream with my partner after the second dance.

17 because I'm an only child, and I don't have a brother to call me 'darling' or a sister to tell me that my hair looks beautiful.

18 and Laura told me to hold on to her, so I wouldn't get lost!

19 because my partner was a much older man.

20 he said something which made me sad, and I wanted to go home.

21 I was worried that no one would ask me to dance.

22 I felt better because I was amazed by the beautiful shining floor, the flowers, and the coloured lights.

Men and Women

~

Children see more than their parents realize. They
may not always understand what they see, but they
have sharp eyes and long ears. They also know when
things aren't right.

The daughter of this house is young enough to
believe in Santa Claus at Christmas – but old enough
to want to fight on her mother's side ...

CLAIRE KEEGAN

Men and Women

Retold by Clare West

My father takes me with him to places. He has artificial hips, so he needs me to open gates. To reach our house, you have to drive up a long narrow road through a wood, open two lots of gates and close them behind you so the sheep won't escape to the road. I'm good at that sort of thing. I get out of the Volkswagen, open the gates, my father drives through, I close the gates behind him and jump back into the passenger seat. To save petrol, he lets the car roll downhill, then starts the engine and we're off to wherever my father is going on that particular day.

He's always looking for a bargain, so sometimes we go to a garage for a cheap spare part for the car. Sometimes we end up in a farmer's dirty field, pulling up young plants we've bought, to take home and grow on our land. On Saturdays my father goes to the market and examines sheep for sale, feeling their bones, looking into their mouths.

If he buys a few sheep, he puts them in the back of the car, and it's my job to keep them there. Da often stops for a meal on the way home. Usually he stops at Bridie Knox's, because Bridie kills her own animals and there's always meat there. The handbrake doesn't work, so when Da parks outside her house, I get out and put a stone behind the back wheel.

I am the girl of a thousand uses.

Bridie lives in a smoky little house, without a husband, but she has sons who drive tractors around the fields. They're small, ugly men whose rubber boots have been mended many times. Bridie wears red lipstick and face powder, but her hands are like a man's.

'Have you a bit of food for the child, missus? There's no food at home,' Da says, making me feel like a starving African child.

'Ah now,' says Bridie, smiling at his old joke. 'That girl looks well-fed to me. Sit down and I'll make some tea.'

'To tell you the truth, missus, I wouldn't say no to a drop of something. I've come from the market, and the price of sheep is shocking, so it is.'

He talks about sheep and cattle and the weather and how this little country of ours is in a terrible state, while Bridie cuts big, thick slices off a large piece of meat. I sit by the window and keep an eye on the sheep in the car. Da eats everything in sight, while I build a little tower of biscuits, lick the chocolate off and give the rest to the sheepdog under the table.

When we get home, I clean out the back of the car where the sheep have been.

'Where did you go?' Mammy asks.

I tell her all about our travels while she and I carry heavy buckets of cattle feed across the yard. Da milks the cow. My brother sits in the sitting room beside the fire and pretends he's studying for his exams next year. My brother is going to be somebody, so he doesn't open gates or clean up dirt or carry buckets. All he does is read and write and do mathematics. He is the intelligent one of the family. He stays in there until he is called to dinner.

'Go and tell Seamus his dinner's on the table,' Da says.

I have to take off my rubber boots before going in.

'Come and have your dinner, you lazy bollocks,' I say.

'I'll tell Da,' he says.

'You won't,' I say, and go to the kitchen, where I put small, sweet garden peas on his plate, because he won't eat boring winter vegetables like the rest of us.

In the evenings, I do my homework on the kitchen table, while Ma watches the television we hire for the winter. On Tuesdays she never misses the programme where a man teaches a woman how to drive a car. Except for a rough woman living behind the hill who drives tractors, no woman we know drives. During the advertising break her eyes leave the screen and travel to the shelf above the fireplace, where she has hidden the spare key to the Volkswagen in an old broken teapot. I am not supposed to know this. I sigh, and continue drawing in the River Shannon on my map.

The night before Christmas, I put up signs. I write THIS WAY SANTA on large pieces of paper. I'm always afraid he will get lost or not bother coming because the gates are too much trouble. I attach the signs to a post at the end of the road, to both gates, and to the door of the sitting room. I put a glass of beer and a piece of cake on the table for him.

Daddy takes his good hat, with a feather in it, out of the cupboard, and puts it on. He looks at himself in the mirror and pulls it on further, to hide his baldness.

'And where are you going?' Mammy asks. 'It's Christmas Eve, a time to stay at home with the family.'

'Going to see a man about a dog,' he says and bangs the door.

I go to bed and have trouble sleeping. I am the only person in my class Santa Claus still visits. But every year I feel there's a greater chance that he won't come, and then I'll be like the others.

I wake early and Mammy is already lighting the fire, smiling. There's a terrible moment when I think maybe Santa didn't come because I said 'you lazy bollocks', but he does come. He leaves me the Tiny Tears doll I asked for, wrapped in the same wrapping paper we have. Santa doesn't come to Seamus any more. I suspect he knows what Seamus is really doing all those evenings in the sitting room, reading magazines and drinking the red lemonade out of the drinks cupboard, not using his intelligence at all.

Only Mammy and I are up. We're the early birds. We make tea, then I help her with the cooking. Sometimes we dance round the kitchen. Seamus comes down to investigate the parcels under the Christmas tree. He gets a dartboard as a present. He and Da throw darts, while

Mammy and I put on our coats and feed the cattle and sheep and look for any newly laid eggs.

'Why don't they do anything to help?' I ask her.

'They're men, that's why,' she says simply.

Because it's Christmas morning, I say nothing. I come inside and a dart flies past my head.

'Ha! Ha!' says Seamus.

'Bulls-eye,' says Da.

The day before New Year, it snows. It is the end of another year. I eat some left-over Christmas food for breakfast and fall asleep watching a film on the television. I get bored playing with my Tiny Tears doll, so I start playing darts with Seamus. When I get a good score, he calls it lucky.

I've had enough of being a child. I wish I was big. I wish I could sit beside the fire and wait to be called to dinner. I wish I could sit behind the wheel of a car and get someone to open the gates for me. Vroom! Vroom! I'd drive away fast.

That night, we get ready for the village dance. Mammy puts on a dark-red dress. She asks me to fasten her pearl necklace for her. She's tall and thin, but the skin on her hands is hard. I wonder if some day she'll look like Bridie Knox, part man, part woman.

Da doesn't make any effort. I have never known him take a bath or wash his hair. He just changes his hat and shoes. Seamus wears a pair of tight black trousers and boots with big heels to make him taller.

'You'll fall over in your high heels,' I say.

We get into the Volkswagen, Seamus and me in the back. Although I washed the inside of the car, I can still smell sheep-dirt. I hate this smell that drags us back to where we come from. Because there are no doors in the back of the car, it's Mammy who gets out to open the gates. I think she's beautiful, with her pearls around her neck and her red skirt flying out as she turns around. I wish Da would get out. I wish the snow would fall on him, not on Mammy in her good clothes. I've seen other fathers holding their wives' coats, holding doors open for them. But Da's not like that.

The village hall stands in the middle of a car park. Inside there's a slippy wooden floor, and benches around the walls, and strange lights that make white clothes seem very bright. Everyone we know is there, including Bridie with her red lipstick, and Sarah Combs, who only last week gave my father a glass of wine and took him into the sitting room to show him her new furniture.

There's a band playing dance music, and Mammy and I are first on the floor. When the music stops and restarts, she dances with Seamus. My father dances with the women he knows from his trips. I wonder how he can dance like that, and not be able to open gates. Old men in their thirties ask me to dance.

They tell me I'm light on my feet. 'Christ, you're like a feather,' they say.

After a while I get thirsty and Mammy gives me money for a lemonade and some raffle tickets. A slow dance begins, and Da walks across to Sarah Combs, who rises from her bench and takes her jacket off. Her shoulders are bare; she looks half naked to me. Mammy is sitting with her handbag on her knees, watching. There is something sad about Mammy tonight; it's all around her, like when a cow dies and the men come to take it away. Something I don't fully understand is happening; a black cloud seems to hang in the air. I offer her my lemonade, but she just drinks a little and thanks me. I give her half my raffle tickets, but she doesn't care. Da has his arms round Sarah Combs, dancing close and slow. I go to find Seamus, who's smiling at a blonde I don't know.

'Go and dance with Sarah Combs instead of Da,' I say.

'Why would I do that?' he asks.

'And you're supposed to be intelligent,' I say. 'Bollocks.'

I walk across the floor and tap Sarah Combs on the back. She turns, her wide belt shining in the light.

'Excuse me,' I say, like when you ask someone the time. She just giggles, looking down at me.

'I want to dance with Daddy,' I say.

At the word 'Daddy' her face changes and she loosens her hold on my father. I take over and dance with him. He holds my hand tight, like a punishment. I can see my mother on the bench, reaching into her bag for a handkerchief. Then she goes to the Ladies' toilets. There's a feeling like hatred all around Da. I get the feeling he's helpless, but I don't care. For the first time in my life I have some power. I can take over, rescue, and be rescued.

There's a lot of excitement just before midnight. Everybody's dancing, knees bending, handbags waving.

The band-leader counts down the seconds to New Year and then there's kissing all round.

My parents don't kiss. In all my life, back as far as I remember, I have never seen them touch. Once I took a friend upstairs to show her the house.

'This is Mammy's room, and this is Daddy's,' I said.

'Your parents don't sleep in the same bed?' she said in amazement. That was when I suspected our family wasn't normal.

The hall's main lights are switched on, and nothing is the same. People are red-faced and sweaty; everything's back the way it is in everyday life. The band-leader calls for quiet, and says the raffle is about to take place. He holds out the box of tickets to the blonde that Seamus was smiling at.

'Dig deep,' he says. 'First prize is a bottle of whiskey.'

She takes her time, enjoying the attention.

'Come on,' he says. 'Christ, girl, it's not a million pounds we're offering!'

She hands him the ticket.

'It's a – what colour would ye say that is? It's a pink ticket, number seven two five and 3X429H. I'll give ye that again.'

It's not mine, but it's close. I don't want the whiskey anyway; I'd rather have the box of Afternoon Tea biscuits that's the next prize. There's a general searching in pockets and handbags. He calls out the numbers a few times and is just going to get the blonde to pick another ticket, when Mammy rises from her seat. Head held high, she walks in a straight line across the floor. A space opens in the crowd; people step to one side to let her pass. I have never seen her do this. Usually she's too shy, gives me the tickets and I run up and collect the prize.

'Do ye like a drop of whiskey, do ye, missus?' the band-leader asks, reading her ticket. 'Sure, it'd keep you warm on a night like tonight. No woman needs a man, if she has a drop of whiskey. Isn't that right? Seven two five, that's the one.'

My mother is standing there in her beautiful clothes and it's all wrong. She doesn't belong up there.

'Let's see,' he says. 'Sorry, missus, the rest of the number's wrong. The husband may keep you warm again tonight.'

My mother turns and walks proudly back, with everybody knowing she thought she'd won. And suddenly she is no longer walking, but running, running in the bright white light towards the door, her hair flowing out like a horse's tail behind her.

Out in the car park it's been snowing, but the ground is wet and shiny in the headlights of the cars that are leaving. Moonlight shines down on the earth. Ma, Seamus, and I sit in the car, shaking with cold, waiting for Da. We can't turn on the engine to heat the car because Da has the keys. My feet are as cold as stones. A cloud of steam rises from the window of the chip van. All around us people are leaving, waving, calling out 'Goodnight!' and 'Happy New Year!' They're buying their chips and driving off.

The chip van has closed down and the car park is empty when Da comes out. He gets into the driver's seat, starts the engine and we're off.

'That wasn't a bad band,' he says.

Mammy says nothing.

'I said, there was a bit of life in that band.' Louder this time.

Still Mammy says nothing.

Da begins to sing 'Far Away in Australia'. He always sings when he's angry. The lights of the village are behind us now. These roads are dark. Da stops singing before the end of the song.

'Did you see any nice girls in the hall, Seamus?'

'Nothing I'd be mad about.'

'That blonde was a nice little thing.'

I think about the market, with all the men looking at the sheep and cattle. I think about Sarah Combs and how she always smells of grassy perfume when we go to her house.

We have driven up the road through the wood. Da stops the car. He is waiting for Mammy to get out and open the gates.

Mammy doesn't move.

'Have you got a pain?' he says to her.

She looks straight ahead.

'Can't you open your door or what?' he asks.

'Open it yourself.'

He reaches over her and opens her door, but she bangs it shut.

'Get out there and open that gate!' he shouts at me.

Something tells me I shouldn't move.

'Seamus!' he shouts. 'Seamus!'

None of us moves.

'Christ!' he says.

I am afraid. Outside, one corner of my THIS WAY SANTA sign has come loose; the sign is hanging from the gate.

Da turns to my mother, his voice filled with hate.

'And you walking up there in your best clothes in front of all the neighbours, thinking you won first prize in the raffle.' He laughs unpleasantly and opens his door. 'Running like a fool out of the hall.'

He gets out and there's anger in his walk. He sings, 'Far Away in Australia!' He is reaching up to open the gate, when the wind blows off his hat. The gate opens. He bends to pick up his hat, but the wind blows it further away. He takes another few steps, but again it is blown just a little too far for him to catch it. I think of Santa Claus using the same wrapping paper as us, and suddenly I understand. There is only one obvious explanation.

My father is getting smaller. The car is rolling, slipping backwards. No handbrake, and I'm not out there, putting the stone in position. And that's when Mammy gets behind the wheel. She moves into my father's seat, the driver's seat, and puts her foot on the brake. We stop going backwards.

And then Mammy starts to drive. There's a funny noise in the engine for a moment, then she gets it right, and we're moving. Mammy is taking us forward, past the Santa sign, past my father, who has stopped singing, through the open gate. She drives us through the snow-covered woods. When I look back, my father is standing there watching our tail-lights. The snow is falling on him, on his bare head, on the hat that he is holding in his hands.

WORD FOCUS

Match each word with an appropriate meaning.

artificial	a flat, thin, dry cake
biscuit	the bones at the side of your body, just below the waist
bollocks	not wearing any clothes
Christ	the sale of numbered tickets, one of which wins a prize
dartboard	an old-fashioned or Irish way of saying 'you'
giggle *(v)*	used when speaking to a woman
hips	man-made, not natural
milk *(v)*	a round board with numbers on it, used in the game of darts (the **bull's eye** is the centre of the dartboard)
missus *(informal)*	someone of bad character; also a rude word meaning 'nonsense'
naked	to laugh in a silly way
raffle *(n)*	an old man with a red coat and a long white beard who, children believe, brings presents at Christmas
Santa Claus	to draw milk from a cow
ye	in this story, an informal *(sometimes offensive)* swear word or exclamation, used to express surprise or anger

The next day in the village, someone is talking about the dance. Use five of the thirteen words from the list to fill in the gaps.

'He says that with two _____ _____, he can't move very well. But he didn't have any trouble dancing with Sarah Combs last night! Did you see her? She was half _____! I feel sorry for his poor wife and little daughter. They do all the heavy work, feeding the cattle and sheep everyday, and all he does is _____ the cow. Last night at the dance, his poor wife thought she'd won the _____, but when they checked her numbers, she hadn't won. She must've felt so embarrassed ... '

Story Focus 1

In a story, the narrator is a character who tells the story. What do you think about the narrator in *Men and Women*? Choose one adjective for the first gap in each sentence, and then write as much as you like to finish the sentences.

angry, anxious, calm, childish, clever, embarrassed, excited, frightened, frustrated, generous, happy, jealous, sad, unhappy

1 I think that the narrator was _____ because _____.
2 The narrator was _____ when _____.
3 The narrator wasn't _____ when _____.
4 When the narrator's father danced with Sarah Combs, she felt _____ because _____.
5 After her mother began to drive the car, I think that the narrator was _____ because _____.

Story Focus 2

Match these halves of sentences to make a paragraph of four sentences. Who do you think the narrator is here?

1 I hate it when he treats her like a servant ...
2 And I get so angry when he treats our son like a little prince ...
3 Even though she's always tired after working with her father, ...
4 Oh, I know she's a clever girl. I hope she studies hard ...

5 ... I make her do her homework every night.
6 ... because I don't want her to have this kind of life when she grows up.
7 ... so that she can escape from this village and live her own life.
8 ... because he'll grow up to treat women just like his father does.

Mr Sing
My Heart's Delight

~

On the west coast of Ireland there are wild, lonely places, where few visitors come. A boy on his yearly visit to his grandmother tells a tale of the old days, a tale of the simple life, when a travelling salesman from a faraway land finds a kindness he did not expect ...

[handwritten: intriguing title]

[handwritten: foreign name or child's mistake]

BRIAN FRIEL

— Mr Sing My Heart's Delight

Retold by Clare West

On the first day of every new year, I made the forty-
five-mile journey by train, post van, and foot
across County Donegal to my grandmother's house. It sat
at the top of a cliff above the wild and stormy Atlantic, at
the very end of a village called Mullaghduff. This yearly
visit, lasting from January until the end of March, was
made mostly for Granny's benefit; during these months
Grandfather went across the water to Scotland to earn
enough money to keep them going for the rest of the year.
But it suited me very well too: I missed school for three
months, I got away from strict parents and annoying
brothers and sisters, and in Granny's house everything I
did was right.

The house consisted of one room, in which Granny
and Grandfather lived and slept. It was a large room lit
by a small window and a door which could be left open
for most of the day, because it faced east and the winds
usually blew from the west. There were three chairs, a
table, a bed in the corner, and an open fire, over which
stretched a long shelf. All the interesting things in the
house were on this shelf – a shining silver clock, two
vases, a coloured photograph of a racehorse, two lifelike
wooden dogs, and three sea-shells sitting on matchboxes

covered with red paper. Every year I went to Granny's, these pieces were handed down to me, one by one, to be inspected, and my pleasure in them made them even more precious to Granny.

She herself was a small, round woman, who must once have been very pretty. She always wore black – a black turning grey with so much washing. But above the neck she was a surprise of strong colour: white hair, sea-blue eyes, and a quick, fresh face, browned by the sun. When something delighted her, she had a habit of shaking her head rapidly from side to side like a child, and although she was over sixty then, she behaved like a woman half her age. She used to challenge me to race her to the garden wall or dare me to go beyond her along the rocks into the sea.

Even on the best day in summer, Mullaghduff is a lonely, depressing place. The land is rocky and bare, and Granny's house was three miles from the nearest road. It was a strange place for a home. But Grandfather was a hard, silent man, who had married Granny when she was a girl of seventeen with a baby daughter (later to become my mother) but no husband. He probably felt he had shown enough kindness by offering to marry her, and the least she could do was accept the conditions of his offer. Or perhaps he was jealous of her prettiness and sense of fun, and thought that the wide ocean behind her and three miles of bare land in front of her would discourage any search for adventure. Whatever his reasons, he had cut her off so completely from the world that at the time of her death, soon after my thirteenth birthday, the longest journey she had ever made was to the town of Strabane, fifty-two miles away.

She and I had wonderful times together. We laughed with one another and at one another. We used to sit up talking until near midnight, and then instead of going to bed, perhaps suddenly decide to eat fish fried in butter or the eggs that were supposed to be our breakfast the next day. Or we would sit round the fire and I would read stories to her from my school reading-book – she could neither read nor write. She used to listen eagerly to these, not missing a word, making me repeat anything she did not understand. After reading, she often used to retell the story to me ('Just to see did I understand right').

And then suddenly she would lose interest in the world outside Mullaghduff and jump to her feet, saying, 'Christ, son, we nearly forgot! If we run to the lower rocks, we'll see the fishing boats from Norway going past. Hurry, son, hurry! They're a grand sight on a fine night. Hurry!'

She had no toys or games for me to play with, but she had plenty of ideas for making my stay with her more interesting. We often got up before sunrise to see wild birds flying north through the icy air high above the ocean. Or we sat for hours on the flat rocks below her house watching the big fish attacking smaller ones in the shallow water. Or we went down to the rock pools and caught fish with our bare hands. I know now that these were all simply Granny's ways of entertaining me, but I am also certain that she enjoyed them every bit as much as I did.

Sometimes we used to watch a great passenger ship sail past, its lights shining like stars. Granny would fill the ship with people for me: 'The men handsome and tall, the ladies in rich silks down to their toes, and all of them laughing and dancing and drinking wine and singing. Christ, son, they're a happy old crowd!'

fantasy / imagination

There was a February storm blowing in from the sea the evening the packman fought his way uphill to our door. I watched him through the kitchen window, a tiny shape in the distance, which grew to a man, and then a man with a case as big as himself.

a pedlar

When he was a stone's throw from the door, I saw that he was coloured. In those days, packmen were quite common in country areas. They went from house to house with their cases of clothes and bedsheets and cheap jewellery, and if a customer had no money to buy, the packmen were usually willing to take food instead. They had a name for being dishonest.

The sight of this packman put the fear of God into me, because Mother had taught us to keep away from all packmen, and I had never seen a coloured man before in my life. I led Granny to the window and hid behind her.

fear of a stranger.

'Will he attack us?' I whispered fearfully.

'Christ, and if he does, we'll attack him back!' she said bravely and threw open the door. 'Come in, man,' she shouted into the storm. 'Come in and rest, because only a fool like yourself could have made the climb up here today.'

He entered the kitchen backwards, dragging his huge case after him. He dropped into a chair near the door, gasping for breath, too exhausted to speak.

I took a step closer to examine him. He was a young man, no more than twenty, with a smooth brown skin. His head was wrapped in a snow-white turban. His shoulders were narrow, and his feet as small as my younger sister's. Then I saw his hands. They were fine and delicate, and on the third finger of his left hand was a gold ring. It was made to look like a snake, holding a deep red stone between its mouth and its tail. As I watched, the stone seemed to change colour: now it was purple, now rose-pink, now black, now blood-red, now blue. I was still staring at its magic when the packman slid to his knees on the floor and began saying in a low, tuneless voice,

'I sell beau-ti-ful things, good lady, everything for your home. What is it you buy? Silks, sheets, beau-ti-ful pictures for your walls, beau-ti-ful dresses for the lady. What is it you buy?'

As he spoke, he opened his case and removed all that it contained, painting the floor with yellows and greens and whites and blues. It seemed to me he owned all the riches of the world.

'You buy, good lady? What is it you buy?' He spoke without interest, without enthusiasm, too exhausted to care. His eyes never left the ground and his hands spread the splashes of colour around him until he was an island in a lake of brightness.

For a moment, Granny said nothing. There was so

much to look at, and it was all so colourful, that she felt quite confused. At the same time she was trying desperately to catch what he was saying, and his accent was difficult for her. When at last words came to her, they broke from her in a sort of cry.

'Ah Christ, sweet Christ, look at them! Look at them! Ah God, how fine they are!' Then rapidly to me, 'What is he saying, son, what? Tell me what it is he's saying.' Then to the packman, 'Ah Christ, mister, they're grand things, mister, grand.'

She knelt down on the floor beside him and gently stroked the surfaces of the clothes. She was silent in amazement, and her mouth opened. Only her eyes showed her delight.

'Try them on, good lady. Try what I have to sell.'

She turned to me to check that she had heard correctly.

'Put on the things you like,' I said. 'Go on.'

She looked at the packman, searching his face to see if he was serious, afraid that he was not.

'I have no money, Mr Packman. No money.'

The packman seemed not to hear. He went on rearranging his colours and did not look up. Only routine kept him going.

'Try them on. They are beau-ti-ful. All.'

She hesitated over the limitless choice.

'Go on,' I said impatiently. 'Hurry up.'

'Everything for the good lady and her home,' said the packman tiredly to the floor. 'Try what I have to sell.'

She made a sudden movement, picking up a red dress

and holding it to her chest. She looked down at it, looked to see what we thought of it, and smoothed it out against her, while her other hand pushed her hair back from her face. Then she was absolutely still, waiting for our opinion.

'Beau-ti-ful,' murmured the packman automatically.

'Beautiful,' I said, anxious to have everything tried on and finished with.

'Beautiful,' echoed Granny, softly, slowly. The word seemed new and strange to her.

Then suddenly she was on her feet, dancing wildly around the kitchen. 'Christ!' she screamed. 'You'd make me as much of a fool as you two are. Look at me! See me in a palace, can you?'

Then she went crazy. She threw the dress on the floor, and tried on one thing after another – a green hat and then white gloves and then a blue jacket, all the time singing or dancing or waving her arms, all the time shaking her head, delighted, ashamed, drunk with pleasure.

But soon she grew tired and threw herself, exhausted, on the bed.

'Now, mister, you can take all the damn things away,' she said breathlessly, 'because I have no money to buy anything.'

Again the packman did not hear her, but said tiredly, 'This you like, good lady.' He opened a tiny box, and inside lay six little silver spoons. 'The box to you, good lady, for half price.'

'Shut your mouth!' she cried, with sudden bitterness,

sitting up on the bed. 'Be quiet, Packman! We are poor people here! We have nothing!'

The packman's head bent lower to the ground and he started to gather his things, ready to go out into the darkness.

At once she was sorry for her bad temper. She jumped off the bed and began building up the fire. 'You'll eat with us, Packman, you'll be hungry. We can offer you … ' She paused and turned to me. 'Christ, son, we'll cook the goose that was to be Sunday's dinner! That's what we'll do!' She turned to the packman. 'Can your stomach hold a good big meal, Packman?'

'Anything, good lady. Anything.'

'A good big meal it'll be, then, and Sunday be damned!'

She took out knives and forks from a drawer. 'Tell me, Packman, what do they call you, what?'

'Singh,' he said.

'What?'

'Singh,' he repeated.

'Christ, but that's a strange name. Sing. Sing,' she said, feeling the sound on her tongue. 'I'll tell you what I'll call you, Packman. I'll call you Mr Sing My Heart's Delight! A good big mouthful, Mr Sing My Heart's Delight!'

'Yes,' he said, quietly accepting her name for him.

'Now, Mr Sing My Heart's Delight, go to sleep for an hour, and when I call you, there'll be a good meal before your eyes. Close your eyes and sleep, you poor exhausted man, you.'

He closed his eyes obediently and in five minutes his head had fallen on his chest.

∾

We ate by the light of an oil lamp. It must have been a month since the packman had last eaten, because he ate fast, like a wild animal, and did not lift his eyes until his plate was cleared. Then he sat back in his seat and smiled at us for the first time.

'Thank you, good lady,' he said. 'A beau-ti-ful meal.'

'You're welcome,' she said. 'Where do you come from, Mr Sing My Heart's Delight?'

'The Punjab,' he said.

'And where might that be?'

'India, good lady.'

'India,' she repeated. 'Tell me, is India a hot country, is it?'

'Very warm. Very warm and very poor.'

'Very poor,' she said quietly, adding the detail to the picture she was making in her mind. 'And oranges and bananas grow there on trees, and the fruit and flowers have all the colours of the rainbow in them?'

'Yes,' he said simply, remembering his own picture. 'It is very beau-ti-ful, good lady. Very beau-ti-ful.'

'And the women,' Granny went on, 'do they wear long silk dresses to the ground? And the men, are the men dressed in purple trousers, and black shoes with silver buckles?'

He spread his hands in front of him and smiled.

'And the women walk under the orange-trees with the

sunlight in their hair, and the men raise their hats to them as they pass … in the sun … in the Punjab … in the Garden of Eden … '

She was away from us as she spoke, leaving us in the bare kitchen, listening to the wind beating on the roof and the ocean crashing below us. The packman's eyes were closed.

'The Garden of Eden,' said Granny again. 'Where the land isn't bare and so rocky that nothing will grow in it. And you have God's sun in that Punjab place and there is singing and the playing of music and the children … yes, the children … ' The first drops of rain came down the chimney and made the fire spit.

'Christ!' she said, jumping to her feet. 'Up you get, you fools, you, and let me wash the dishes.'

The packman woke with a start, and bent to pick up his case.

'And where are you going?' she shouted to him. 'Christ, man, a wild animal wouldn't be out on a night like this! You'll sleep here tonight. There – in front of the fire. Like a cat,' she added, with a shout of laughter. The packman laughed too.

By the time we had washed the dishes, it was bedtime. Granny and I undressed quickly in the shadowy end of the room, and jumped into the big bed which we always shared.

'Blow out the lamp, Mr Sing My Heart's Delight,' said Granny, 'and then place yourself on the floor there. You'll find a bit of carpet near the door if you want to lie on that.'

'Good night, good lady,' he said. 'Very good lady.'

'Good night, Mr Sing My Heart's Delight,' she replied.

He put the old piece of carpet in front of the fire and stretched himself out on it. Outside, the rain beat against the roof, and inside, the three of us were comfortable and warm.

It was a fine morning the next day. The packman looked young and bright, and his case seemed lighter too. He stood outside the door, smiling happily as Granny directed him towards the villages where he would have the best chance of selling his things. Then she wished him goodbye, in the old Irish way.

'God's speed,' she said, 'and may the road rise with you.'

'To pay you I have no money, good lady,' he said, 'and my worthless things I would not offer you, because ... '

'Go, man, go. There'll be rain before dinnertime.'

The packman still hesitated. He kept smiling like a shy girl.

'Christ, Mr Sing My Heart's Delight, if you don't go soon, you'll be here for dinner and you ate it last night!'

He put his case on the ground and looked at his left hand. Then, taking off the ring with his long, delicate fingers, he held it out to her.

'For you,' he said very politely. 'Please accept from me ... I am grateful.'

Even as it lay on his hand, the stone changed colour several times. It had been so long since Granny had been offered a present that she did not know how to accept it. She bent her head and whispered, 'No. No. No.'

'But please, good lady. Please,' the packman insisted. 'From a Punjab gentleman to a Donegal lady. A present. Please.'

When she did not come forward to accept it, he moved towards her and took her left hand in his. He chose her third finger and put the ring on it. 'Thank you, good lady,' he said.

Then he lifted his case, and turned towards the main road. The wind was behind him and carried him quickly away.

Neither of us moved until we could no longer see him. I turned to go round to the side of the house; it was time to feed the chickens and milk the cow. But Granny did not move. She stood looking towards the road with her arm and hand still held as the packman had left them.

'Come on, Granny,' I said crossly. 'The cow will think we're dead.'

She looked strangely at me, and then away from me and across the road and up towards the mountains in the distance.

'Come on, Granny,' I said again, pulling at her dress.

As she let me lead her away, I heard her saying to herself, 'I'm thinking the rain will get him this side of Crolly bridge, and then his purple trousers and silver-buckled shoes will be destroyed. Please God, it will be a fine day. Please God it will.'

WORD FOCUS

Choose words from the list to complete these sentences (one word for each gap). There are nine words in the list, but only eight of them will be needed.

buckles, Christ, coloured, depressing, drag, Garden of Eden, goose, snake, turban

1 When Granny was excited or angry, she often said '_____'. This word is used as an informal (and sometimes offensive) swear word or exclamation, to express surprise or anger.

2 The packman was from India, and he did not have white skin. The narrator had never seen a _____ man before in his life.

3 The packman wore a _____, which is a long piece of cloth around the head, worn, for example, by Sikh and Muslim men.

4 When the packman arrived at the house, he was so exhausted that he had to _____ his huge case after him.

5 For dinner, Granny cooked a _____, which is a large bird like a duck, but bigger.

6 Granny thought that the Punjab in India was like the _____ (in the Bible), the beautiful place where Adam and Eve lived; a place of innocence and happiness.

7 The packman gave Granny a ring, which was in the shape of a _____, an animal with a very long thin body and no legs.

8 Granny thought that all the men in the Punjab wore purple trousers and black shoes with silver _____.

STORY FOCUS 1

The setting of a story is where the story takes place. This might be in a city, like Paris or London, or in a jungle, on a ship at sea, or even in space. In some stories, the setting is very important.

1 Describe the setting of *Mr Sing My Heart's Delight* in two or three sentences, giving as many details as you can.

2 Do you think that the setting is important to this story? Why, or why not? Explain your answer to a partner.

STORY FOCUS 2

Imagine that the narrator is now grown up, married with a new baby, and living in a town. He and his wife don't have much money, so they are talking about moving into Granny's old home, which is now empty after Grandfather's recent death. What should they do? Fill in the chart, giving at least two reasons for each side.

STAY IN TOWN	MOVE TO GRANNY'S
1	1
2	2

Death Wish

~

There are certain dreams which a psychiatrist knows can indicate a death wish in a patient, a decreasing wish to live, and a desire for suicide. People with a death wish often like high places – cliffs, tall buildings, bridges …

The Morrissey Bridge crosses a deep river which cuts the city in two. It is late at night. Fog is rising off the water, and a man leans over the bridge, a man with dark thoughts of suicide on his mind …

Think it is going to be melancholy instead mystery murder clever title

LAWRENCE BLOCK

Death Wish

Retold by John Escott

American

The cop saw the car stop on the bridge but didn't think too much about it. People often stopped their cars on the bridge late at night, when there was not much traffic. The bridge was over the deep river that cut the city neatly in two, and the center of the bridge provided the best view of the city.

Suicides liked the bridge, too. The cop didn't think of that until he saw the man get out of the car, walk slowly along the footpath at the edge, and put a hand on the rail. There was something about that lonely figure, something about the grayness of the night, the fog coming off the river. *uncertainty* The cop looked at him and swore, and wondered if *& urgency* he could get to him in time.

He didn't want to shout or blow his whistle because he knew what shock or surprise could do to a probable suicide. Then the man lit a cigarette, and the cop knew he had time. They always smoked all of that last cigarette before they went over the edge. *experience*

When the cop was within ten yards of him, the man *nervous* turned, gave a slight jump, then nodded as if accepting that the moment had passed. He appeared to be in his middle thirties, tall with a long narrow face and thick *detail* black eyebrows.

58

non threatening

passage

'Looking at the city?' said the cop. 'I saw you here, and thought I'd come and have a talk with you. It can get lonely at this hour of the night.' He patted his pockets, pretending to look for his cigarettes and not finding them. 'Got a spare cigarette on you?' he asked.

The man gave him a cigarette and lit it for him. The cop thanked the man and looked out at the city.

'Looks pretty from here,' he said. 'Makes a man feel at peace with himself.'

'It hasn't had that effect on me,' the man said. 'I was just thinking about the ways a man could find peace for himself.' *to take this into yr own hands*

'Things usually get better sooner or later, even if it takes a little while,' the cop said. 'It's a tough world, but it's the best we've got, and you're not going to find a better one at the bottom of a river.'

The man said nothing for a long time, then he threw his cigarette over the rail and watched it hit the water. *why give* He turned to face the cop. 'My name's Edward Wright. I *his name?* don't think I'd have done it. Not tonight.'

'Something particular bothering you?' said the cop. *upsetting /*
'Not … anything special.' *disturbing*
'Have you seen a doctor? That can help, you know.'
'So they say.'
'Want to get a cup of coffee?' said the cop.

The man started to say something, then changed his mind. He lit another cigarette and blew out a cloud of smoke. 'I'll be all right now,' he said. 'I'll go home, get some sleep. I haven't been sleeping well since my wife—'

now he understands

'Oh,' the cop said.

'She died. She was all I had and, well, she died.'

kind,
sympathetic

The cop put a hand on his shoulder. 'You'll get over it, Mr Wright. Maybe you think you can't live through it, that nothing will be the same, but—'

'I'd better get home,' the man said. 'I'm sorry to cause trouble. I'll try to relax, I'll be all right.'

The cop watched him drive away and wondered if he should have taken him into the police station. But if you started taking in everyone who thought about suicide, you'd never stop. He went back towards the other side of the bridge. When he reached it, he took out his note-book

imp
details

and wrote down the name, *Edward Wright.* So he would remember what the man meant, he added, *Big Eyebrows, Wife Dead, Thought About Jumping.*

∞

The psychiatrist stroked his pointed beard and looked at the patient.

' … no longer worth living,' the man was saying. 'I

Mr Wright
again

almost killed myself the night before last. I almost jumped from the Morrissey Bridge.'

'And?'

'A policeman came along. I wouldn't have jumped anyway.'

'Why not?'

'I don't know.'

The endless talk of patient and doctor went on. Sometimes the doctor went through a whole hour without thinking at all, making automatic replies but not really hearing a word that was said to him. *I wonder*, he thought, *whether I do these people any good at all. Perhaps they only want to talk, and need a listener.*

He listened next to a dream. Almost all his patients told him their dreams, which annoyed the psychiatrist, who never remembered having a dream of his own. He listened to this dream, glancing now and then at his watch and wishing the hour would end. The dream, he knew, indicated a decreasing wish to live, a development of the death wish, and a desire for suicide that was prevented only by fear. But for how long?

Another dream. The psychiatrist closed his eyes and stopped listening. Five more minutes, he told himself, and then this fool would leave.

∞

repeated
detail

The doctor looked at the man, saw the heavy eyebrows, the expression of guilt and fear.

'I have to have my stomach pumped, Doctor,' the man said. 'Can you do it here or do we have to go to a hospital?'

'What's the matter with you?'

'Pills.'

'Sleeping pills? How many did you take?'

'Twenty,' said the man.

'Ten can kill you,' said the doctor. 'How long ago did you take them?'

'Half an hour. No, maybe twenty minutes.'

'And then you decided not to act like a fool, yes? Twenty minutes. Why wait this long?'

'I tried to make myself sick.'

'Couldn't do it? Well, we'll try the stomach pump,' the doctor said.

It was very unpleasant, but finally the doctor said, 'You'll live.'

'Thank you, Doctor.'

'Don't thank me. I'll have to report this.'

'I wish you wouldn't. I'm … I'm under a psychiatrist's care. It was more an accident than anything else, really.'

The doctor raised his eyebrows. 'Twenty pills? You'd better pay me now. I can't risk sending bills to people who may be suicides.'

∞

'This is a fine gun for the price,' the clerk said. 'But for just a few dollars more—'

'No, this will be satisfactory. I'll need a box of bullets.'

The clerk gave him a box. 'Or three boxes for—'

'Just the one.'

The shopkeeper opened a book. 'You'll have to sign there, to keep the law happy.' He checked the signature when the man had finished writing. 'I'm supposed to see something to identify you, Mr Wright. Can I see your driver's license?' He checked the license, compared the signatures, and wrote down the license number.

'Thank you,' said the man.

'Thank you, Mr Wright. I think you'll get a lot of use out of that gun.'

'I'm sure I will.'

passage

At nine o'clock that night, Edward Wright heard his back
doorbell ring. He walked downstairs, glass in hand,
finished his drink and went to the door. He was a tall
man with thick black eyebrows. He looked outside,
recognized his visitor, and opened the door.

His visitor put a gun in Edward Wright's stomach.

'Mark—'

'Invite me in,' the man said. 'It's cold out here.'

'Mark, I don't—'

'Inside.'

In the living room, Edward Wright stared at the gun
and knew that he was going to die.

'You killed her, Ed,' the visitor said. 'She wanted a
divorce. You couldn't let her have that, could you? I told
her it was dangerous to tell you, that you were nothing but
an animal. I told her to run away with me and forget you
but she wanted to do the right thing, and you killed her.'

'You're crazy!'

'You made it look like an accident, didn't you? How
did you do it? Tell me, or this gun goes off.'

'I hit her.' Wright looked at the gun, then at the man.
'I hit her a few times, then I threw her down the stairs.
You can't go to the police with this, you know. They can't
prove it and they wouldn't believe it.'

'We won't go to the police,' the man said. 'I didn't go
to them at the beginning. They didn't know of a motive
for you, did they? I could have told them a motive, but
I didn't go, Edward. Sit down at your desk. Take out a

*Tells him
readily
&
clinically*

piece of paper and a pen. There's a message I want you to write.'

'You can't—'

'Write *I can't go on any longer. This time I won't fail,* and sign your name.' He put the gun against the back of Edward Wright's shaking head.

'You'll hang for it, Mark.'

'Suicide, Edward.'

'No one will believe I was a suicide, note or no note. They won't believe it.'

'Just write the note, Edward. Then I'll give you the gun and leave you to do what you must do.'

'You—'

'Just write the note. I don't want to kill you, Edward. I want you to write the note, and then I'll leave you here.'

Wright did not exactly believe him, but the gun at his head left him little choice. He wrote the note and signed his name.

'Turn round, Edward.'

He turned and stared. The man looked very different. He had put on false eyebrows and false hair, and he had done something to his eyes.

'Do you know who I look like now, Edward? I look like *you.* Not exactly like you, of course, but a good imitation of you.'

'You – you've been pretending to be me? But why?'

'You just told me you're not the suicidal type, Edward. But you'd be surprised at your recent behavior. There's a policeman who had to talk you out of jumping off the

Morrissey Bridge. There's the psychiatrist who has been seeing you and hearing you talk about suicide. There's the doctor who had to pump your stomach this afternoon. It was most unpleasant. I was worried my false hair might slip, but it didn't. All those things you've been doing, Edward. Strange that you can't remember them. Do you remember buying this gun this afternoon?'

'I—'

'You did, you know. Only an hour ago. You had to sign for it. Had to show your driver's license, too.'

'How did you get my driver's license?'

'I didn't. I created it.' The man laughed softly. 'It wouldn't fool a policeman, but no policeman saw it. It fooled the clerk though. Not the suicidal type? All those people will swear you are, Edward.'

'What about my friends? The people at the office?'

'They'll all help. They'll start to remember your moods. I'm sure you've been acting very shocked and unhappy about her death. You had to play the part, didn't you? You should never have killed her, Edward. I loved her, even if you didn't. You should have let her go, Edward.'

Wright was shaking with fear. 'You said you weren't going to murder me. You were going to leave me with the gun—'

'Don't believe everything you hear,' the man said, and, very quickly, he pushed the gun into Wright's mouth and shot him. Afterwards, he arranged things neatly, wiped his own fingerprints from the gun and put Wright's fingerprints on it. He left the note on top of the desk, put the psychiatrist's business card into Wright's wallet, and the receipt for the gun into Wright's pocket.

'You shouldn't have killed her,' he said to Wright's dead body. Then, smiling privately, he went out of the back door and walked off into the night.

a way of finding peace

Dis questions

What did the title make you think of?

What did you think of the first few paragraphs / the first page / the opening of the story.

How do the first 2 paras set the scene?

As you were reading, how did you think it would end?

What other crime or mystery stories have you read?

✓ **Connections** – places known for suicides, taking revenge

Words · bothering p59   talk you out of p64

✓ **Passages** p59.   p63   p64

Culture – buying a gun
         imp. of dreams
         visiting a psychiatrist

WORD FOCUS

On the way to the bridge, perhaps Mark went over the details of his plan in his mind. Use these words to complete his thoughts (one word in each gap). There are three extra words which will not be needed.

clerk, cop, divorce, fingerprints, glance, motive, murder, pills, pretend, prove, psychiatrist, pump, suicide

'I think I've thought of everything. In a few days, everyone will believe that Edward has been thinking about _____. I know the police car stops near the bridge every night at this time, so tonight I'll get out of the car and make sure that the _____ notices me. Then, tomorrow, I have another appointment with the _____ I've been seeing, and I'll tell him some more of my dreams. I'm sure he believes already that 'Edward' is sick in his mind.'

'Then I'll go to a doctor and tell him I've taken too many _____ , so he'll have to _____ my stomach to get the pills to come out. That will be a second doctor who knows that 'Edward' is thinking about killing himself. Finally, when I buy the gun, my signature will be required by law, and the _____ will have to check my identity. So he'll have a record of 'Edward' too.'

'I know Edward's clever. The police would never find a _____ for him to _____ her. None of this would have to happen if he'd given her a _____ . He didn't love her, but I did. He shouldn't have killed her. Now, he's going to pay … I must remember to wipe my _____ from the gun and to put his fingers on it … '

taking justice into yr own hands.

debate
Edgar Allan Poe , Amontillado
— revenge

STORY FOCUS

Here are three short passages from the story. Read them, and answer the questions.

> 'It hasn't had that effect on me,' the man said. 'I was just thinking about the ways a man could find peace for himself.'

1 Who says these words in the story, and to whom?
2 Where does this conversation take place?
3 What do you think the speaker means by *the ways a man could find peace for himself*?

> ' ... no longer worth living,' the man was saying. 'I almost killed myself the night before last. I almost jumped from the Morrissey Bridge.'

4 Who says these words in the story, and to whom?
5 Why do you think the speaker confesses to almost jumping off the bridge?
6 Do you think the listener believes the speaker? Why, or why not?

> 'I wish you wouldn't. I'm ... I'm under a psychiatrist's care. It was more an accident than anything else, really.'

7 Who says these words, and to whom?
8 Where does this conversation take place?
9 What does the 'it' refer to in *it was more an accident*?

Cooking the Books

Many people dream of owning their own business, a shop, or perhaps a restaurant. And they believe that good ideas and hard work will one day bring them financial success. But the reality of running a business can be very different from the dream.

Mr Haldeman, a restaurant owner, is a troubled man, a man whose dream has turned into a nightmare. But he has a plan to save himself from financial ruin – a simple plan, a perfect plan, a plan that cannot possibly go wrong …

Cooking the Books

Retold by John Escott

a plan

Haldeman had left nothing to chance. When he stepped out of his office on Friday evening, he walked through the restaurant instead of going straight down to the garage. He stopped to talk for a few minutes with José and the head waiter, as if it were just the end of another quiet week.

On the way home he was surprised to find that he was sweating, even though it was quite cool inside the car. Haldeman looked at himself in the car mirror, and what he saw disturbed him. A forty-eight-year-old man whose once-round face had grown thin with worry, whose shirt collars were now two sizes too big. Even his wedding ring was loose on his finger. His suit fitted badly across his shoulders. It was years old, but how could he afford to buy a new one? When Mona left him, she said she would take every dollar of his money, but how could she take what he didn't have?

reality! unreality?

He stopped the Toyota in front of his apartment building. It was a beautiful evening. In Los Angeles the evenings were always beautiful, but this one also held the promise of escape.

Haldeman went up to his apartment where he mixed himself a drink and went over the details of his plan.

The truth was, he was facing financial ruin. With each week that passed, the restaurant earned less and less. Who could say why? It had been a great idea, even Mona had agreed. With the small amount he had saved, and the money from Mona, he had managed to convince the bank to lend him an equal amount to start a restaurant specializing in barbecued food.

Each evening at five, 'Haldeman's', the blue and purple sign above the restaurant, lit up the Los Angeles sky. The position had seemed perfect, right on the corner of La Cienega and Santa Monica Boulevard. José, the chef, was excellent, the waiters were eager to please, yet something had gone wrong. The fashionable crowd had moved away to downtown restaurants, and without them to pay crazy prices, how could he hope to pay his bills? Add to that the money needed for his apartment, for his ex-wife Mona, for his gambling debts – yes, he had started gambling again – and you had the picture of a man moving fast towards disaster.

Haldeman finished his drink and went to the bedroom to pack. If he left soon, he would arrive in Palm Springs in time for a relaxing dinner at that new Japanese place on Highway 111. It shouldn't take him more than two and a half hours to drive there tonight. Nobody else would be going that way at this time of the year. He silently thanked the gods for sending him someone as stupid as Larry Hyatt. Silly, harmless, never-say-no Hyatt, who was about to play his part in a plan so simple and perfect that nothing – *nothing* – could possibly go wrong.

Haldeman loaded up the car and drove away from the apartment building. Already he was beginning to feel better, although he would not be able to celebrate until tomorrow evening, when he would arrive back in Los Angeles to find his restaurant burnt to the ground. He drove out of Los Angeles, past hotels and factories, until he reached the desert.

Haldeman had only visited Palm Springs once before, but he liked it and thought it was the ideal place to be while his plan was carried out. He turned on to Bob Hope Drive and drove towards Rancho Mirage, at the far end of Palm Springs. He thought about his plan yet again. The secret, he decided, was getting other people to do the dangerous work for you. All you needed was simple, loyal people who trusted you, like Larry Hyatt. And like José, the chef.

Hyatt had been employed by Haldeman as business manager for two years, and because of his unquestioning trust in his employer, he had produced completely false accounts for the last financial year. It had been simple enough to arrange.

According to the computer in Hyatt's office, the restaurant had enjoyed its best profits ever, with more customers in the last month than ever before. Hyatt rarely came to the restaurant. He knew little of the Mexican workers who were paid almost nothing, or of the nights when there was not a single customer. His accounts were based on false information and wage packets that did not exist. Even when the figures had been put into the computer, they were not safe from Haldeman, who had carefully altered them, just a little at a time. Poor old Hyatt never suspected a thing.

Why pretend the restaurant was making a profit? So that the insurance company would not suspect anything when they came to check the accounts of a recently burnt-down restaurant. They'd have suspicions about a place if business was bad. But a place as successful as this? Never!

Haldeman parked in front of the Ranchero Motel. It was an old wooden building which needed painting. It had ten small rooms set around a courtyard, and a swimming pool that was rarely cleaned. But for Haldeman, there couldn't be a better place.

The man behind the desk wore a sweat-stained T-shirt and had a day-old beard. Haldeman wrote his name in the guest book, making sure that his writing was clear and the date was correct. He knew the book would be checked. It was obvious that he was the only person staying at the Ranchero Motel. You had to be crazy to come to Palm Springs in August. It was a time when the relaxing warmth of the dry desert air turned to a fierce heat.

Haldeman put his bag in his room, then drove downtown and ate a large, expensive meal. He returned to the motel with some beer in one hand and a bucket of ice in the other.

The next day, his plan would begin. If he had any

doubts about it, now was the time to stop the whole thing. But there was no other answer to his problems. He had to go ahead with it. He went into his room and opened a beer.

∞

Haldeman was woken at six-thirty by the sun on his face. He turned over on to his stomach. The sheets on the bed were a mess and he was sweating already.

In eight and a half hours, José would light the burners beneath the barbecue in the kitchen to prepare for the evening customers. At the same moment, Larry Hyatt had orders to call Haldeman from the manager's office above the restaurant. Haldeman had given Larry the phone number of the motel on Friday. He had also given him a small job to do at the restaurant on Saturday afternoon. This ensured that Larry would be in the building as the crime took place, and as the restaurant began to burn.

Haldeman climbed out of bed, smiling. Before he left on Friday, he had partly blocked the gas taps on the kitchen burners so that when they were turned off for the night, two of the taps would remain half open. All the pipes under the barbecue would then slowly fill with gas. There would be no leak to the outside air, only a large amount of gas in the system just waiting for José to come and light it at three o'clock this afternoon.

Hyatt, calling from the manager's office, would probably be far enough away from the explosion not to get hurt. Unlike José, who would be blown to pieces.

Of course, there was always the chance that José would

decide to light the gas early today, but that didn't matter. Hyatt would have more reason to phone his boss quickly, and Haldeman would still have his alibi confirmed by the phone call. He got dressed and opened the door of his room. The heat from outside hit him like a solid wall. He looked at his watch. Seven thirty-five. It wasn't surprising that nobody came here in August.

He walked over to the pool and put a hand into the water. It felt hot to his hand. All around the sun beat down on to the trees and buildings, and the air was heavy and still.

Haldeman drove out to a nearby café for breakfast and afterwards took a walk around town before returning to his car. Shop windows were dark and their doors had signs which read: SEE YOU IN SEPTEMBER! The effort of walking around in this fierce heat was too much and he returned to the motel. When he arrived, he found the front office open and went in.

'Hi!' said old Ricky, the motel manager. His face still needed a shave. 'You sleep OK last night?'

'I guess so. Didn't expect it to be so hot this morning.' Haldeman sat down in a chair by the desk. 'What do you think the temperature is?'

'Oh, a hundred and ten, hundred and fifteen, about now,' said Ricky, looking out of the window. 'You just wait till after lunch though, if you want to feel some *real* heat. It'll be up in the hundred and twenties by then.'

'Why do you stay here in August?' asked Haldeman.

'I have to get this place ready for when we get busy

again. I'm having a new roof put on, and new tar and tiles put down in the courtyards where the ground's cracked open with the heat. I have to almost rebuild this place every summer. We get storms, and floods, and heatwaves in August that kill half the old people. You want a beer?' He pushed an ice-cold can of beer along the desk.

A short time later, Haldeman returned to his room. While he was waiting for his call, he decided to sit and read outside under one of the faded orange sunshades surrounding the swimming pool. After only a few minutes, he was asleep.

The book fell to the ground and Haldeman woke up. He was suddenly thirsty. Beyond the blue pool stood rows of trees, and beyond those lay the desert, and then the mountains. Somewhere over toward the front office, hidden by trees, Mexican workmen called to each other as they carried in new orange tiles ready for repairing the courtyard.

He got up and walked back to his room. Inside it was cool and dark. A quarter to one. Two and a quarter hours before José reduced his restaurant to a car park, and Haldeman was provided with a solid, unbreakable alibi. He would have to make sure he was near a phone when Hyatt's call came through.

It was at this point that Haldeman noticed the lack of a telephone in the room.

danger to his plan.

෴

'No, sir, one thing we haven't got yet is room phones,' said Ricky, picking at his teeth with a piece of paper. He sat behind the reception desk with what was left of a plate of fried chicken in front of him. 'We don't get asked for them. People come here to get away from them.'

'Listen, I'm expecting a very important phone call in a couple of hours,' said Haldeman. 'I gave them the number here … '

'Where did you get that from?' asked Ricky.

'From the telephone book.'

'Oh, *that* number, that's the old number.'

'You mean I won't get the call?'

'Oh, it rings here still, but it's out the back on the old pay phone now. We changed the numbers last year.'

Haldeman sat back, relieved. 'Where can I find the phone booth?' he asked, trying to sound as casual as possible.

'Just go out behind the workmen to the back courtyard and it's straight across.'

'Thanks. I'll see you later.' Haldeman got up from the chair and went out into the sun.

At two thirty, he left his room with a beach towel and a glass filled with ice and whisky. He knew he probably shouldn't drink whisky before the call, but he needed it.

Round the back of the motel he found a large courtyard. Along one side a pair of faded sun-beds stood in the shadow of the wall. In the opposite far corner of the courtyard stood the phone booth, little more than a pay phone on a metal stick. Below it, a faded phone book hung on a chain.

The heat in the courtyard was amazing. Protected

from the desert winds, it lay sheltered and silent at the back of the motel grounds. Haldeman lay down on one of the sun-beds. After a few minutes, he fell into a half-sleep, and began to imagine the chef coming into the restaurant. He would be surprised to see Hyatt there, and the two men would talk together for a minute or two. José would then walk on to the kitchen, put on his chef's clothes, and wash his hands. Meanwhile, Hyatt would move up to the manager's office and sit at the desk with his papers. Haldeman turned on to his side and drank the whisky before lying back on the sun-bed.

It was so hot here, hot enough to start a barbecue restaurant that worked on the natural heat of the sun … yes, maybe that was what he would do … maybe …

The phone was ringing.

Haldeman sat up on the sun-bed and looked at his watch. It was exactly three o'clock. He must have fallen asleep. Jumping up, he looked around for his shoes and shirt, then across at the ringing telephone on the far side of the courtyard. He wiped his sweating face. The ground between him and the telephone would be burning hot, but he would have to run across. He couldn't afford to miss the call; his alibi depended on it.

He ran towards the telephone booth, running as lightly as possible, but had only taken three steps before becoming aware of something wrong. The pain which had begun to cut into his bare feet was obviously caused by the sun-baked ground, but the ground did not feel solid under his feet. At the next step the bottom of his right foot felt as if it was on fire, and he screamed. In the distance, the telephone rang on. He looked down and saw the floor of the courtyard boiling in the heat, and this time he was forced to pull his left leg forward to keep moving. The sharp movement tore a piece of skin from the bottom of his left foot, and he fell forward on to one hand and a knee, crying with pain.

He could see the telephone, no more than eight feet away, ringing and ringing. All around him the surface of the courtyard was boiling. The Mexican workmen had only finished putting down the new tar yesterday. They had covered the surface with sand, then moved on to another part of the grounds. But because of the fierce heat, the tar had failed to harden. And today, the sun had brought the tar back to an almost liquid state.

Unable to support his body on his burning hand and knee, Haldeman fell screaming, face down onto the courtyard. Liquid knives of fire burned into his skin. He tried to turn and pull himself free, but every time he moved more skin tore loose …

Larry Hyatt slowly put down the telephone. That was strange. Haldeman had particularly asked him to call at this time. As it happened, he needed to speak to the boss anyway, as there was a problem with the restaurant. An hour ago, José the chef had called to say he was sick, and so far they had been unable to find another chef. It looked as if they would not be able to open at all tonight. Oh well, he would try again in a few minutes.

Haldeman was stuck by his bleeding, raw face in the hot tar. His chest, knees, and legs were also stuck, and the more he struggled, the more he stuck. His screams became higher and higher as the hot black liquid finally touched his right eye and boiled it white.

When the telephone rang again, he was still alive, though not conscious. Blood and tar had dried across his torn back, and most of the skin from his head and body lay stuck in the tar.

Altogether Hyatt rang four times, and for the first three Haldeman was still alive. But then the sun pushed up the temperature a further few burning degrees.

The red thing that had been Haldeman moved for the last time as the sound of the telephone faded in its ears, and the chances of healing its torn body in the coolness of the motel's reception office disappeared in the cruel, unforgiving heat.

WORD FOCUS

Match each word with an appropriate meaning. Then use some of the words to complete the sentences below.

alibi

alter (altered)

barbecue

chef

courtyard

insurance

motel

profit

stick (stuck)

sweat

tar

a professional cook

to become fixed to something with a sticky substance

a thick black sticky liquid used in making roads

liquid that appears on your skin when you are very hot or ill

to change, to make (something) different

an outdoor meal where food is cooked on an open fire

a hotel for people travelling by car, with space for car parking near the rooms

an open space enclosed by the walls of buildings

money paid to protect yourself against the cost of a possible disaster

the proof that you were elsewhere when a crime happened

the money that you make in business or by selling things, especially after paying the costs involved

1 Haldeman went to a _____ in Palm Springs because he needed an _____ for the time of the planned explosion at the restaurant.

2 Haldeman wanted to burn down the restaurant so that he would get the _____ money.

3 Hyatt did not know that Haldeman had _____ the figures in the computer to produce completely false accounts for the restaurant.

4 The restaurant was not making a _____ – it was losing money every month.

5 When Haldeman went to answer the phone, he didn't realize that the _____ was in an almost liquid state.

STORY FOCUS 1

Here are two different endings for the story. Choose the idea you like best, and then use the notes to write a paragraph for your new ending.

1 / restaurant burns to ground / chef dies / Hyatt escapes / police investigate / Haldeman alibi / Hyatt suspicious / false accounts / insurance money / Haldeman arrested /

2 / restaurant burns to ground / chef and Hyatt die / police investigate / accident / gas company blamed / insurance money / starts new Chinese restaurant / very successful /

STORY FOCUS 2

After Haldeman's death, perhaps the police interviewed the workers at the restaurant. Match these halves of sentences to make a paragraph of five sentences. Who do you think the narrator is here?

1 Yes, I enjoyed working for Haldeman's restaurant …
2 And yes, I always believed him to be an honest man, …
3 When he told me he was going to Palm Springs, …
4 Before he left for Palm Springs, he gave me a phone number …
5 No, he never told me that he had a large insurance policy on the restaurant, …

6 … and asked me to call him at three o'clock on Saturday.
7 … but now I'm wondering if there was a reason for his sudden trip.
8 … so I had no idea he was putting false figures into the accounts.
9 … because the work was easy and the business made a nice profit.
10 … I did wonder why – no one goes there in August, it's too hot.

The Stolen Body

~

Ghosts, spirits, apparitions – these things do not usually belong in the world of scientific research and enquiry. But it is not always clear where the natural world ends and the supernatural begins.

In London, in the late 1890s, two serious men, Mr Bessel and Mr Vincent, begin an experiment in thought transfer. They want to discover if it is possible to use the power of thought to send an apparition through space. It is an experiment that leads to an unknown and terrifying world …

H. G. WELLS

The Stolen Body

Retold by John Escott

Mr Bessel was a partner in the company Bessel, Hart, and Brown, of St Paul's Churchyard. Among those researchers concerned with the study of the mind, he was known as a very thorough investigator, but also as someone always prepared to listen to new ideas. He was unmarried and occupied rooms in the Albany, near Piccadilly. He was particularly interested in the transfer of thought and in apparitions of the living. In November 1896, he and Mr Vincent, of Staple Inn, began experiments to see if it was possible to send an apparition of themselves through space, by the power of thought.

At an arranged time, Mr Bessel shut himself in one of his rooms in the Albany and Mr Vincent in his living room in Staple Inn. Each then fixed his thoughts on the other, and Mr Bessel attempted, by the power of thought, to transfer himself as a 'living ghost' across the space of two miles to Mr Vincent's apartment. On several evenings this was tried without any satisfactory result, but on the fifth or sixth attempt, Mr Vincent did actually see or imagine he saw an apparition of Mr Bessel standing in his room. He noticed that Mr Bessel's face was white, his expression was anxious, and his hair was untidy. For a moment Mr Vincent was too surprised to speak or move,

84

and in that moment the figure seemed to glance over its shoulder and disappear.

They had arranged to attempt to photograph any apparition, but Mr Vincent was too slow to use the camera on the table beside him. However, excited by the first sign of success, he wrote down the exact time and at once took a taxi to the Albany to tell Mr Bessel.

He was surprised to find Mr Bessel's outside door open to the night, and lights on in the apartment. More surprising than this, a champagne bottle lay smashed on the floor, a table had been pushed over, and there were black fingermarks on the walls. One of the curtains had been torn down and thrown on to the fire and the smell of burning filled the room.

A shocked Mr Vincent hurried to the porter's house at the entrance to the Albany. 'Where is Mr Bessel?' he asked. 'Do you know that all the furniture is broken in his room?'

The porter said nothing, but came to Mr Bessel's apartment. When he saw the mess, he said, 'I didn't know about this. Mr Bessel's gone away. He's mad!'

He then explained that half an hour previously (at about the time of Mr Bessel's apparition in Mr Vincent's rooms) Mr Bessel had rushed out of the gates of the Albany into Vigo Street and disappeared in the direction of Bond Street.

'And as he went past me,' the porter said, 'he laughed, a sort of gasping laugh, with his mouth open and his eyes staring. He waved his hand, with the fingers bent like claws, and he said in a sort of fierce whisper, *"Life!"* Just that one word, *"Life!"'*

'Oh dear,' said Mr Vincent.

He waited for some time but Mr Bessel did not return. After leaving a note, he returned to his own rooms, unable to think of an explanation for Mr Bessel's behaviour. He tried to read but could not, so he went to bed early. When at last he fell into an uneasy sleep, it was at once disturbed by an upsetting dream.

He saw Mr Bessel waving his arms wildly, his face white and afraid. He even believed that he heard his friend calling to him for help. He woke up and lay trembling in the darkness. And when he finally went to sleep again, the dream returned and was even more frightening than before. He awoke with a strong feeling that Mr Bessel was in some terrible danger and needed his help. Further sleep was impossible so, although it was still dark, he got up and dressed, then went out towards Vigo Street to see if Mr Bessel had returned.

As he was going down Long Acre, something made him turn towards Covent Garden market, which was just starting to open. He heard shouting, then saw someone turn the corner and run towards him. He knew at once that it was Mr Bessel – but a much-changed Mr Bessel. He had no hat, his clothes were untidy, and his shirt collar was torn open. He held a walking-stick by the wrong end, and his mouth was pulled into a strange shape.

'Bessel!' cried Vincent.

The running man gave no sign of recognizing either

Mr Vincent or his own name. Instead, he hit his friend in the face with the stick. Mr Vincent fell on to the pavement and, when he looked again, Mr Bessel had disappeared. A policeman and several market porters were running after him towards Long Acre.

Mr Vincent got up and was immediately the centre of a crowd of people, anxious to help him and to tell him about the 'madman'. He had suddenly appeared in the middle of the market screaming, '*Life! Life!*', hitting left and right with a blood-stained walking-stick, and dancing and shouting with laughter. A boy and two women had broken heads, and he had smashed a man's wrist. Next he had taken a lamp from a coffee shop and thrown it through the post office window before running away laughing.

Mr Vincent wanted to run after his friend and save him from the angry people chasing him. But then news came through the crowd that Mr Bessel had got away.

Mr Vincent returned to his rooms angry and puzzled. It seemed that Mr Bessel must have gone violently mad in the middle of the thought transfer experiment, but why did that make him appear with a sad white face in Mr Vincent's dreams?

He shut himself carefully in his room, lit his fire, washed his injured face, and tried without success to read until night became day. Only then did he go to bed and sleep.

He got up late, his bruised face in considerable pain. There was nothing about Mr Bessel in the morning newspapers and, after a visit to the Albany, where nothing had changed, he went to see Mr Hart, Mr Bessel's partner and friend.

Mr Vincent was surprised to learn that Mr Hart, although he knew nothing of what had happened to his friend, had also been disturbed by dreams of Mr Bessel, white-faced and apparently begging desperately for help.

'I was just going to go and see him at the Albany when you arrived,' said Mr Hart. 'I was sure that something was wrong with him.'

The two men decided to ask about their missing friend at the police station. Here they learned that the police had not caught Mr Bessel, but that he had gone on to smash windows along Tottenham Court Road, had hit a policeman in Hampstead Road, and had then attacked a woman.

All this happened between half past twelve and quarter to two in the morning. In fact, there was evidence of Mr Bessel's violence through London from the moment he ran from his rooms at half past nine in the evening. But after a quarter to two, when he had been seen running down towards Baker Street, he had suddenly disappeared.

All that day and all that night, Mr Vincent waited for news, but none came. In his dreams that night he again saw Mr Bessel's desperate, tear-stained face, and he also saw other faces, shadowy but evil, that seemed to be chasing Mr Bessel.

It was on the next day, Sunday, that Mr Vincent thought of Mrs Bullock, the medium, who was becoming famous in London at that time. She was staying at the house of Dr Wilson Paget.

Mr Vincent went to the house, but he had hardly mentioned the name of Bessel when Dr Paget interrupted him.

'He communicated with us last night!' said Dr Paget. 'It was at the end of the seance.'

He left the room and returned with a large piece of paper, on which were five words, written by an unsteady hand. But Mr Vincent recognized the writing. It was Mr Bessel's.

'How did you get this?' he asked.

Dr Paget explained. During the seance Mrs Bullock passed into a state of trance, during which she received a message that she wrote on the piece of paper with her left hand.

George Bessel ... Baker Street ... help ...

Strangely, neither Dr Paget or the other two people who were present had heard of the disappearance of Mr Bessel. They had put the piece of paper with the many other mysterious messages that Mrs Bullock had delivered.

When Dr Paget heard Mr Vincent's story, he got to work at once to investigate this clue. And indeed, it proved to be a good clue as the missing Mr Bessel was found at the bottom of a large hole near Baker Street Station.

The hole is part of the work to prepare for the new electric railway, and it is protected by a fence nearly twenty feet high. Somehow, Mr Bessel must have climbed this fence before falling down the hole. His arm and leg were broken, but his madness had left him. He was, of course, very weak, and when he saw his rescuers arrive, he could not stop himself crying with relief. He was taken to a doctor's house in Baker Street and given something to help him sleep. But on the second day he gave a statement, which he has since repeated several times.

To understand it clearly, it is necessary to go back to his experiments with Mr Vincent. Mr Bessel says that he did actually, by the power of thought alone, leave his body and pass into some place or state outside this world.

'At one moment I was sitting in my chair with my eyes tightly shut,' he says, 'fiercely concentrating my mind on Vincent. Then I saw myself outside my body – saw my body near me, but not containing me. I felt I had become a kind of cloud, attached to but not part of my physical body. I could see the Albany and Piccadilly and Regent Street, and all the rooms in the houses, very small and very bright, spread out below me like a little city seen from the sky. What amazed me most is that I saw quite clearly the insides of the houses – saw people eating and drinking, talking, playing cards. I could see everything that went on.'

Those were Mr Bessel's exact words. Forgetting Mr Vincent, he remained for a time observing these things. Then, becoming curious, he reached down with a shadowy arm and attempted to touch a man walking along Vigo Street. But he could not do it, though his finger seemed to pass through the man. Something prevented him, but he finds it difficult to describe what it was. He compares it to a sheet of glass, which stopped him getting through to the physical world again. But one thing impressed him immediately. He was in a world without sound.

His first concern was where he might be. He was out of his physical body, but that was not all. He also believed that he was somewhere out of space altogether. By an enormous effort of thought, he had passed out of his body into a world beyond this world. A world not dreamed of, yet in some strange way lying so close that all things on this earth are clearly visible, both from outside and from within.

It was then he remembered Mr Vincent and turned his mind to travelling in this new body. For a time he was attached to his physical body, and his new strange cloud-body could not break free from it. Then quite suddenly he was free. For a moment everything was hidden by what seemed to be dark clouds. Then, through a break in the clouds, he saw his body fall away, and he was moving along in a strange place of shadowy clouds with London spread out beneath them.

But now he became aware that it was not clouds surrounding him, it was *faces!* Faces of thin shadow, with evil, greedy eyes and ugly smiling lips. Their cloud-like hands tried to catch him as he went past, and the rest of their bodies faded away into the darkness. No sounds came from their mouths. The shadowy Mr Bessel, now filled with terror, passed through this silent moving crowd of eyes and reaching hands.

So ghostly were these faces, so evil their staring eyes, that Mr Bessel did not think of speaking to them. Their expressions were of envy and a hungry desire for *life*.

And yet, even among these noiseless evil things, he could still think of Mr Vincent. He made a violent effort of thought and suddenly found himself moving towards Staple Inn.

He saw Vincent sitting in his chair by the fire, and for a time he tried to get in front of his friend's eyes, to move objects in his room, to touch him. But Mr Vincent was not aware of him. That strange something that Mr Bessel compared to a sheet of glass separated them.

And at last Mr Bessel did a desperate thing. He could see not only the outside of a man but also *within*, so he reached out his shadowy hand into, it seemed, his friend's brain.

Mr Vincent sat up suddenly and in an instant Mr Bessel knew that he had been seen. At the same moment Mr Bessel knew that a great evil had happened to his body. He immediately forgot Mr Vincent and flew back to the Albany, and the countless surrounding faces flew with him, like leaves before a storm.

But he was too late. The body he had left – lying there like a dead man – had stood up, using some strength beyond his own. Now it stood with staring eyes, stretching its arms.

For a moment Mr Bessel watched, then he moved towards it. But the sheet of glass stopped him again, and the evil faces around him laughed. The little, round, middle-aged body that had once been his was now dancing with mad delight, throwing his furniture around, tearing his books, smashing bottles.

He watched all this in terrified amazement. Then, with the evil faces crowding round him, he hurried back to Vincent to tell him of the dreadful thing that had happened to him.

But the brain of Vincent was now closed against apparitions as he hurried out into Holborn to call a taxi. Defeated and full of terror, Mr Bessel again flew back to find the body he had left. It was running and shouting happily down the Burlington Arcade. It had Mr Bessel's body, but it was not Mr Bessel. It was an evil spirit out of that strange world beyond our own.

For twenty hours it held possession of Mr Bessel's body, and during that time Mr Bessel's cloud-body, or spirit, was in that mysterious middle world of shadows, looking for help. He spent many hours trying to enter the minds of Mr Vincent and of his friend Mr Hart, but without success. And all the time he was terrified that the body would be killed by its furious owner, and he would have to remain in this shadow-land for ever.

Mr Bessel was not the only human spirit in that place. He met several shadows of men like himself who had lost their bodies and who were wandering in that lost world that is neither life nor death. They could not speak because that world is silent, but he knew that they were men because of their shadowy human shapes, and the sadness of their faces.

But how had they come into that world? And where were their lost bodies? Dr Wilson Paget believes that they are the sane spirits of those men who are lost in madness on earth.

At last Mr Bessel came to a place where a little crowd of spirits was gathered. Pushing through them, he saw below a brightly lit room. In this room were four or five men, and a woman sitting awkwardly in a chair with her head thrown back. It was Mrs Bullock, the medium. And he could see a strange light – sometimes bright, sometimes faint – moving about inside her brain. She was talking, and at the same time writing with one hand. And Mr Bessel saw that the human spirits around him were all trying desperately to touch these lighted parts of her brain. When one managed to do this, or another was pushed away, her voice and her writing changed, confusing the spirit messages and making them impossible to understand. But suddenly Mr Bessel understood what was happening. The woman spoke for the spirit that touched her.

Desperately he began to struggle towards her, but he was on the outside of the crowd and could not reach her. So he went away to find out what was happening to his body.

After a long time, he found it at the bottom of a hole in Baker Street with its leg and arm broken. At once Mr Bessel returned to Mrs Bullock and the seance. It was almost finished and many of the shadows were going away in despair. Mr Bessel struggled through them and managed to reach the woman's brain. And in that moment she wrote down the message that Dr Paget kept. After that, the other shadows pushed Mr Bessel away.

He went back to Baker Street and waited, watching the evil spirit inside the body swearing and crying with pain. Then, as the night changed to day, the brain shone brightly and the evil spirit came out. And Mr Bessel entered the body he had feared he would never enter again. As he did this, the long silence ended, and he heard the traffic and the voices of people above him. And that strange world that is a shadow of our world – the dark and silent shadows of desire and the shadows of lost men – disappeared.

It was three hours before he was found in that dark, damp place, crying and in pain. But his heart was full of joy. He was back once more in the kindly world of men.

adj.

adv: kindly

WORD FOCUS

Use the clues below and complete this crossword with words from the story.

		1									
				2				3		4	
						5					
6											
7											
		8									

ACROSS

5 The _____ at the Albany believed that Mr Bessel had gone mad.

7 An _____ is an image of a person who is not present.

8 Mr Vincent and Mr Bessel were conducting an _____, which had unexpected results.

DOWN

1 When he went into Mr Bessel's apartment, Mr Vincent found some broken furniture and a _____ bottle smashed on the floor.

2 Mrs Bullock was a _____; she could communicate with the spirit world.

3 Mrs Bullock went into a _____, a state in which you appear to be asleep but are aware of things around you.

4 A _____ is a meeting at which people try to make contact with the spirit world.

6 Dr Paget believed that the human spirits in the shadow-land were the _____ spirits of men who had gone mad on earth.

STORY FOCUS

After his wounds were treated, Mr Bessel returned to his apartment, and the police went at once to speak with him. Match the officer's questions with Mr Bessel's answers to make their conversation.

Police Officer's questions:

1 'Mr Bessel, we'd like to ask you some questions now.'
2 'What were you doing in your apartment on the night when you ran wildly into the street and started attacking people?'
3 'I see, Mr Bessel. How did you plan to send this, er, apparition?'
4 'And do you think your experiment was a success?'
5 '*Your body* attacked those people? You mean, *you* attacked them.'
6 'Mr Bessel, how much champagne had you drunk that evening?'
7 'We will continue these questions tomorrow, Mr Bessel. And tomorrow, we would like to know the truth.'

Mr Bessel's answers:

8 'None at all, officer. The champagne in my apartment is only kept for guests. You must believe me. *I* didn't hurt those people.'
9 'Oh, no, it wasn't me. I wasn't in my body. When I took my spirit out of my body, you see, an evil spirit moved in and occupied it.'
10 'But this *is* the truth! I promise you, every word of it is true!'
11 'Well, partly. I did manage to transfer my spirit, but the result of this was that my body began attacking those innocent people.'
12 'Mr Vincent and I were conducting an experiment. I was trying to send him an apparition of myself through space.'
13 'By the power of thought. We sat in our own apartments, fixing our thoughts on each other. Then, I tried to transfer myself as a "living ghost" to Mr Vincent's apartment.'
14 'Yes, very well. I will do my best to help you.'

About the
Authors

LAWRENCE BLOCK

Lawrence Block (1938–) was born in Buffalo, New York. He published his first crime story at the age of nineteen, and since then he has written more than fifty novels and over a hundred short stories. His most famous character is probably Matt Scudder, an ex-cop who works as a private investigator in New York. His other creations include Bernie Rhodenbarr, a burglar who solves crimes, and Keller, assassin and stamp-collector. Most of Block's novels are set in New York City, where he has lived for decades.

Lawrence Block is one of the most respected and bestselling names in crime and mystery fiction. He is a Grand Master of Mystery Writers of America, and has won countless mystery awards in many countries, including the Cartier Diamond Dagger for Life Achievement from the Crime Writers Association in the UK.

With his wife Lynne, Block spends a lot of time travelling – they have visited more than a hundred and twenty countries – but New York is his home. He said in an interview in 2004: 'I grew up in upstate New York, in Buffalo. But I remember when I was ten, my father and I took the train to New York for a long weekend, and I probably fell in love with it then. As soon as I could, I moved here, and I've lived most of my adult life in New York. It's my town.'

About the Authors

CHRISTOPHER FOWLER

Christopher Fowler (1953–) is a Londoner, who was born in Greenwich in south-east London, and now lives in King's Cross in the city centre. He knew from an early age what he wanted to do. 'I started writing as soon as I was old enough to hold a pen. I still have the old books I filled. It's all I ever wanted to do.' From schooldays he was a great fan of horror, fantasy, and science fiction, and he put his enthusiasm for writing to good use by writing letters to newspapers. 'When I was very young,' he said in an interview, 'writing was a good way of fiddling extra pocket money. I used to write to Letters Pages that paid £5 for the Star Letter.'

After studying at art college, he worked in advertising, and then at the age of twenty-four, he co-founded The Creative Partnership, a movie marketing organization. He divides his time between his film business and his writing. His many bestselling novels include *Roofworld*, *Red Bride*, *Spanky*, and *Psychoville*, and he has published ten collections of short stories. His writing combines elements of black comedy, anxiety, and social satire, and as well as thrillers and horror stories, he has written a series of mystery novels, about the adventures of two elderly detectives called Bryant and May. He also writes film scripts, newspaper articles, and reviews. An autobiography, *Paperboy*, was published in 2009.

Many of Fowler's stories are set in London, and in his blog he writes, 'I choose London as the backdrop of many stories because any one of the events in its two-thousand-year history can provide inspiration for a story.'

101

BRIAN FRIEL

Brian Friel (1929–) was born in Omagh in Northern Ireland, and spent the early part of his life in Derry, also in Northern Ireland, where he became a teacher like his father before him. In 1960 he stopped teaching and became a full-time writer, and in 1969 he moved to County Donegal in Ireland, a place he knew well and loved deeply. His writing career began with short stories, and he published two collections in the 1960s. The story *Mr Sing My Heart's Delight* comes from the collection *The Saucer of Larks* (1962).

Brian Friel is one of Ireland's most famous playwrights. His first major success was *Philadelphia, Here I Come!* in 1964, and he went on to write many more plays, which have been performed with great success in Dublin, London, and New York. In 1981, *Translations* was awarded the Ewart-Biggs Peace Prize, and *Dancing at Lughnasa* (1990), probably his most successful play, won several awards and has also been filmed.

In 1980, Friel and actor Stephen Rea started the Field Day Theatre Company, whose purpose was to produce plays for an Irish audience rather than for theatres in New York or London. They took their plays to many towns in Ireland because they felt they 'wanted to be heard by their own people'.

Friel has received many awards for his work, but remains a very private man, who has made few personal statements. In his *Self Portrait* he says, 'I am married, have five children, live in the country, smoke too much, fish a bit, read a lot, worry a lot, get involved in sporadic causes and invariably regret the involvement, and hope that between now and my death I will have acquired a religion, a philosophy, a sense of life that will make the end less frightening than it appears to me at the moment.'

CLAIRE KEEGAN

Claire Keegan (1968–) was born in County Wicklow in Ireland and grew up on a farm, the youngest of six children. She left home at seventeen to study English and Political Science at a university in New Orleans, USA, and returned to Ireland in 1992.

She wrote her first short story in 1994 when she was unemployed. She needed money, so she sent her story to a competition that was run by a television programme. 'There were 10,000 entries,' she said in an interview, 'and my story was in the top ten. That gave me encouragement and I said maybe I'll be good at this.' She returned to university to study Creative Writing, and continued to write short stories. She says, 'I find the short story form deeply attractive ... There is a strictness about it which I really admire, and it takes your breath away if it's good.'

Her stories have been highly praised and have won many awards. Her first short story collection, *Antarctica* (1999), which includes the story *Men and Women*, won the 2000 Rooney Prize for Irish Literature. Her second collection, *Walk the Blue Fields* (2007), won the Edge Hill award. At a talk at the Edinburgh Festival in 2007, she described the role that the domestic setting plays in her writing. 'It is a huge part of our lives. I am very interested in what people do at home when they are alone. Usually it's very little. So much of our life isn't lived – our private lives are going on in our heads. This is why reading is like nothing else. I'm drawing the dots but the reader is linking these dots with personal thoughts.'

KATHERINE MANSFIELD

Katherine Mansfield (1888–1923) was born Kathleen Mansfield Beauchamp in Wellington, New Zealand. Her father was a wealthy banker, and Katherine, with her brother and three sisters, had a comfortable life as a child. At the age of fourteen she was sent to London to finish her education, and she spent most of the rest of her short life in Europe.

From an early age, Katherine felt different from her family. She studied music for a time, and was already writing stories while still at school. She spent her life among writers and artists, and her friends included some famous authors of the time, such as D. H. Lawrence and Virginia Woolf.

Although she married twice, Katherine never lived an ordinary family life. From the age of twenty, she suffered from a serious disease, and in search of better health, she spent part of every year in France and Switzerland. She wrote a large number of short stories, even though it was often difficult for her to find the strength and peace she needed in order to write. She died in France, aged only thirty-five.

Her first book, *In a German Pension*, appeared in 1911, followed by *Prelude* in 1916, *Bliss* in 1921, and *The Garden Party and Other Stories* in 1922. Two more books of stories, her letters, and her journal were published after her death.

She is considered to be one of the finest writers of her time, and has often been compared to the Russian writer Chekhov. Her sensitive, delicate stories take the reader straight into the lives of her characters, who are often women struggling to survive in an unfriendly world.

H. G. WELLS

Herbert George Wells (1866–1946) was born in Kent in the south-east of England. When he was seven years old, he broke his leg in an accident. He passed the time by reading books, which his father brought him from the local library, and he became so interested in other worlds and lives that he decided to be a writer. He worked hard to educate himself, and for a time was a teacher and a journalist before achieving fame through writing.

Wells was an imaginative social and political thinker, and wrote a great many books on history, social commentary, and science, but he is best remembered today for his science-fiction stories. Novels such as *The Time Machine* (1895), *The Invisible Man* (1987), *The War of the Worlds* (1898), and *The First Men in the Moon* (1901) marked the beginning of what we know as science fiction. He also wrote more than eighty short stories; the most famous of these is probably *The Country of the Blind*.

Many of Wells's novels and stories have been filmed, some more than once. A crater on the far side of the moon has been named after him, and there is an H. G. Wells Society. More than a hundred years later, his novels still excite interest, and Wells and the French writer Jules Verne are each sometimes referred to as 'the Father of Science Fiction'.

Towards the end of his life, after two World Wars, Wells became pessimistic about the future, and wrote: 'While there is a chance of the world getting through its troubles, I hold that a reasonable man has to behave as though he were sure of it. If at the end your cheerfulness is not justified, at any rate you will have been cheerful.'

READING CIRCLE ROLES

When you work on your role sheet, remember these words:

~ READ ~ THINK ~ CONNECT ~ ASK ~~ AND CONNECT

READ ~

• Read the story once without stopping.
• Read it again while you work on your role sheet.

THINK ~

• Look for passages in the story that are interesting or unusual. Think about them. Prepare some questions to ask about them.
• Think about the meanings of words. If you use a dictionary, try to use an English-to-English learner's dictionary.

CONNECT ~

• Connect with the characters' thoughts and feelings. Perhaps it is a horror story and we cannot 'connect' with an experience like this, but we can see how the characters are thinking or feeling.

ASK ~

• Ask questions with many possible answers; questions that begin with *How? Why? What? Who?* Do not ask *yes/no* questions.
• When you ask questions, use English words that everyone in your circle can understand, so that everyone can talk about the story.

AND CONNECT ~

• Connect with your circle. Share your ideas, listen to other people's ideas. If you don't understand something, ask people to repeat or explain. And have fun!

The role sheets are on the next six pages (and on page 121 there are role badges you can make). Bigger role sheets, with space for writing, are in the Teacher's Handbook. Or you can read about your role in these pages, and write your notes and questions in your own notebook.

Discussion Leader

STORY: _____

NAME: _____

The Discussion Leader's job is to . . .

• read the story twice, and prepare at least five general questions about it.
• ask one or two questions to start the Reading Circle discussion.
• make sure that everyone has a chance to speak and joins in the discussion.
• call on each member to present their prepared role information.
• guide the discussion and keep it going.

Usually the best discussion questions come from your own thoughts, feelings, and questions as you read. (What surprised you, made you smile, made you feel sad?) Write down your questions as soon as you have finished reading. It is best to use your own questions, but you can also use some of the ideas at the bottom of this page.

MY QUESTIONS:

1 _____

___ _____

___ _____

___ _____

___ _____

___ _____

___ _____

Other general ideas:

• Questions about the characters (*like / not like them, true to life / not true to life ...?*)
• Questions about the theme (*friendship, romance, parents/children, ghosts ...?*)
• Questions about the ending (*surprising, expected, liked it / did not like it ...?*)
• Questions about what will happen next. (These can also be used for a longer story.)

Summarizer

STORY: _____

NAME: _____

The Summarizer's job is to . . .

• read the story and make notes about the characters, events, and ideas.
• find the key points that everyone must know to understand and remember the story.
• retell the story in a short summary (one or two minutes) in your own words.
• talk about your summary to the group, using your writing to help you.

Your reading circle will find your summary very useful, because it will help to remind them of the plot and the characters in the story. You may need to read the story more than once to make a good summary, and you may need to repeat it to the group a second time.

MY KEY POINTS:

Main events:
Characters:

MY SUMMARY:

Connector

STORY: _____

NAME: _____

The Connector's job is to . . .

- read the story twice, and look for connections between the story and the world outside.
- make notes about at least two possible connections to your own experiences, or to the experiences of friends and family, or to real-life events.
- tell the group about the connections and ask for their comments or questions.
- ask the group if they can think of any connections themselves.

These questions will help you think about connections while you are reading.
Events: Has anything similar ever happened to you, or to someone you know? Does anything in the story remind you of events in the real world? For example, events you have read about in newspapers, or heard about on television news programmes.
Characters: Do any of them remind you of people you know? How? Why? Have you ever had the same thoughts or feelings as these characters have? Do you know anybody who thinks, feels, behaves like that?

MY CONNECTIONS:

1 _____

___ _____

___ _____

___ _____

___ _____

___ _____

___ _____

___ _____

___ _____

Word Master

STORY: _____

NAME: _____

The Word Master's job is to . . .

• read the story, and look for words or short phrases that are new or difficult to understand, or that are important in the story.
• choose five words (only five) that you think are important for this story.
• explain the meanings of these five words in simple English to the group.
• tell the group why these words are important for understanding this story.

Your five words do not have to be new or unknown words. Look for words in the story that really stand out in some way. These may be words that are:

• repeated often   • used in an unusual way   • important to the meaning of the story

MY WORDS	MEANING OF THE WORD	REASON FOR CHOOSING THE WORD
_____ PAGE _____ LINE _____		
_____ PAGE _____ LINE _____		
_____ PAGE _____ LINE _____		
_____ PAGE _____ LINE _____		
_____ PAGE _____ LINE _____		

Passage Person

STORY: _____

NAME: _____

The Passage Person's job is to . . .

• read the story, and find important, interesting, or difficult passages.
• make notes about at least three passages that are important for the plot, or
that explain the characters, or that have very interesting or powerful language.
• read each passage to the group, or ask another group member to read it.
• ask the group one or two questions about each passage.

A passage is usually one paragraph, but sometimes it can be just one or two
sentences, or perhaps a piece of dialogue. You might choose a passage to
discuss because it is:

• important • informative • surprising • funny • confusing • well-written

MY PASSAGES:

PAGE _____ LINES _____

REASONS FOR CHOOSING THE PASSAGE	QUESTIONS ABOUT THE PASSAGE

PAGE _____ LINES _____

REASONS FOR CHOOSING THE PASSAGE	QUESTIONS ABOUT THE PASSAGE

PAGE _____ LINES _____

REASONS FOR CHOOSING THE PASSAGE	QUESTIONS ABOUT THE PASSAGE

Culture Collector

STORY: _____

NAME: _____

The Culture Collector's job is to . . .

• read the story, and look for both differences and similarities between your own culture and the culture found in the story.
• make notes about two or three passages that show these cultural points.
• read each passage to the group, or ask another group member to read it.
• ask the group some questions about these, and any other cultural points in the story.

Here are some questions to help you think about cultural differences.

Theme: What is the theme of this story (for example, getting married, meeting a ghost, murder, unhappy children)? Is this an important theme in your own culture? Do people think about this theme in the same way, or differently?

People: Do characters in this story say or do things that people never say or do in your culture? Do they say or do some things that everybody in the world says or does?

MY CULTURAL COLLECTION (differences and similarities):

1 **PAGE** _____ **LINES** _____ : _____

_____

2 **PAGE** _____ **LINES** _____ : _____

_____

MY CULTURAL QUESTIONS:

— _____
— _____
— _____
— _____

113

PLOT PYRAMID ACTIVITY

A **plot** is a series of events which form a story. The Reading Circles **Plot Pyramid** is a way of looking at and talking about the plot of a story. The pyramid divides the story into five parts.

The Exposition gives the background needed to understand the story. It tells us who the characters are, where the story happens, and when it happens. Sometimes we also get an idea about problems to come.

The Complication is the single event which begins the conflict, or creates the problem. The event might be an action, a thought, or words spoken by one of the characters.

The Rising Action brings more events and difficulties. As the story moves through these events, it gets more exciting, and begins to take us toward the climax.

The Climax is the high point of the story, the turning point, the point of no return. It marks a change, for better or for worse, in the lives of one or more of the characters.

The Resolution usually offers an answer to the problem or the conflict, which may be sad or happy for the characters. Mysteries are explained, secrets told, and the reader can feel calm again.

HOW TO PLOT THE PYRAMID

1 Read your story again, and look for each part of the pyramid as you read. Make notes, or mark your book.

2 In your Reading Circle, find each part of the pyramid in the story, and then write down your ideas. Use the boxes in the diagram opposite as a guide (a bigger diagram, with space for writing in the boxes, is in the Teacher's Handbook).

3 Begin with the *Exposition*, and work through the *Complication*, the *Rising Action* (only two points), the *Climax*, and the *Resolution*.

4 Finally, your group draws the pyramid and writes the notes on the board, and then presents the pyramid to the class.

_____ STORY TITLE _____

4 Climax
This is when ____
This is the Climax because ____

CLIMAX

3 Rising Action
The two most important
points are ____
They are important
because ____

RISING
ACTION

2 Complication
This is when ____
This is the Complication
because ____

EXPOSITION

RESOLUTION

COMPLICATION

1 Exposition
The important
points are ____

5 Resolution
This is when ____
This is the Resolution
because ____

POSTER ACTIVITY

Each Reading Circle group makes a poster in English about a story in this book. Posters can have words, pictures, and drawings. Your group will need to find extra information about the story – perhaps from the Internet, or the school library, or your teacher.

Use the ideas on the opposite page to help you. When all the posters are finished, each Reading Circle will present their own poster to the other groups. At the end, keep all the posters, and make a 'poster library'.

STORY TITLE

_____

THE THEME
What is the theme of the story?

• Is it about love or murder or friendship? Is it about dreams or wishes or fears?

THE TIME, THE PLACE
What do you know about the time and the place of the story?

• the city / the country?
• a real world, or an unreal world?
• If the time and place are not given, does it matter?

THE WRITER
What interesting facts do you know about the author's life?

• Was he or she also a poet, an actor, a teacher? Or a spy, a sailor, a thief, a doctor, a madman?

THE BACKGROUND
What cultural information did you learn from the story?

• About family events (for example, a wedding)
• A national holiday
• Family life (for example, parents and children)

THE LANGUAGE
What did you like about the language in the story?

• Find a quotation you like – words that are funny or clever or sad, or words that paint a picture in your mind.

THE FILM
Direct your own film! Who will play the characters in the film?

• Choose the best actors to play the characters.
• Where will you film it?
• Will you change the story?
• What title will the film have?

BOOKWORMS CLUB
Stories for Reading Circles
Editor: Mark Furr

The Bookworms Club brings together selections of adapted short stories at different levels from other Bookworms titles. These stories have been specially chosen for use with Reading Circles.

BOOKWORMS CLUB BRONZE
STAGES 1 AND 2

The Horse of Death by Sait Faik, from *The Meaning of Gifts: Stories from Turkey*

The Little Hunters at the Lake by Yalvac Ural, from *The Meaning of Gifts: Stories from Turkey*

Mr Harris and the Night Train by Jennifer Bassett, from *One-Way Ticket*

Sister Love by John Escott, from *Sister Love and Other Crime Stories*

Omega File 349: London, England by Jennifer Bassett, from *The Omega Files*

Tildy's Moment by O. Henry, from *New Yorkers*

Andrew, Jane, the Parson, and the Fox by Thomas Hardy, from *Tales from Longpuddle*

BOOKWORMS CLUB SILVER
STAGES 2 AND 3

The Christmas Presents by O. Henry, from *New Yorkers*

Netty Sargent and the House by Thomas Hardy, from *Tales from Longpuddle*

Too Old to Rock and Roll by Jan Mark, from *Too Old to Rock and Roll and Other Stories*

A Walk in Amnesia by O. Henry, from *New Yorkers*

The Five Orange Pips by Sir Arthur Conan Doyle, from *Sherlock Holmes Short Stories*

The Tell-Tale Heart by Edgar Allan Poe, from *Tales of Mystery and Imagination*

Go, Lovely Rose by H. E. Bates, from *Go, Lovely Rose and Other Stories*

BOOKWORMS CLUB GOLD
STAGES 3 AND 4

The Black Cat by Edgar Allan Poe, from *Tales of Mystery and Imagination*
Sredni Vashtar by Saki, from *Tooth and Claw*
The Railway Crossing by Freeman Wills Crofts, from *As the Inspector Said and Other Stories*
The Daffodil Sky by H. E. Bates, from *Go, Lovely Rose and Other Stories*
A Moment of Madness by Thomas Hardy, from *The Three Strangers and Other Stories*
The Secret by Arthur C. Clarke, from *The Songs of Distant Earth and Other Stories*
The Experiment by M. R. James, from *The Unquiet Grave*

BOOKWORMS CLUB PLATINUM
STAGES 4 AND 5

No Morning After by Arthur C. Clarke, from *The Songs of Distant Earth and Other Stories*
The Nine Billion Names of God by Arthur C. Clarke, from *The Songs of Distant Earth and Other Stories*
Across the Australian Desert by Robyn Davidson, from *Desert, Mountain, Sea*
Casting the Runes by M. R. James, from *The Unquiet Grave*
The Songs of Distant Earth by Arthur C. Clarke, from *The Songs of Distant Earth and Other Stories*
Feuille d'Album by Katherine Mansfield, from *The Garden Party and Other Stories*
The Doll's House by Katherine Mansfield, from *The Garden Party and Other Stories*

ROLE BADGES

These role icons can be photocopied and then cut out to make badges or stickers for the members of the Reading Circle to wear.